AUGURIES

of

THINGS TO COME

Poems & Prose

Also by Linda Strever

Against My Dreams: An Immigrant's Story (poetry)

Don't Look Away (novel)

My Life in Cars (poetry)

For Glenn,

In gratitude for your support and for Lee's many gifts in my life.

Lila
2023

AUGURIES

—— *of* ——

THINGS TO COME

Poems & Prose

Linda Strever

Lila Strever

PAINTED SNAKE PRESS

Olympia, Washington

LindaStrever.com

ISBN 978-0-9896228-2-0

Cover and book design by Debi Bodett
DebiBodett.com

Back cover oak tree and interior acorn and leaf images
from Freepik.com

Author photo by Barry Troutman

Printed in the United States of America

First Edition
Published by Painted Snake Press
Olympia, Washington

For my ancestors

and for the land

To My Readers

This is a work of fiction, inspired by my ancestral heritage and by historical events. Through poetry and short prose, it tells a powerful story about how the living land provides and about what survives through generations across time and place.

The character **BILL** is based on my father, who was a prisoner of the Germans in World War II, captured in December 1944 during the Battle of the Bulge.

LENA, who opens the book, is Bill's daughter. Her observations, memories, and revelations are echoes of mine.

AGNES, the book's main character, is named for my 6th-great-grandmother, Agnes Dietrich, who emigrated in 1710 from the Lower Palatinate, a feudal principality in what is now Germany.

Woven into Agnes's story are historically accurate experiences of early Palatine immigrants, whose long and arduous journey eventually brought them to the Schoharie Creek Valley in upstate New York, then a British colony and the traditional lands of the Haudenosaunee (Iroquois) people.

GARNET, Agnes's daughter, carries the wisdom and knowledge passed down by women through millennia.

Hour of smoke

Hour of need

Hour of bread

Hour of seed

Contents

To My Readers. vii

PRESS RELEASE:
Gundestrup Cauldon Reunited with Missing Piece. 3

PART 1: Hour of Smoke
  Lena, 1997-1998. 5

PART 2: Hour of Need
  Bill, 1944-1945. 19

PART 3: Hour of Bread
  Agnes, 1705-1763. 29

  1. *The Turning*
  Rhine River Valley, 1705-1709. 31

  2. *Night and Day at Sea*
  Aboard Ship, 1710. 49

  3. *Arrival*
  Schoharie Valley, British Colonial New York,
  1712-1714. 65

  4. *Good Days*
  1714-1715. 91

  5. *The Land Speaks*
  1722. 109

6. *Then and Now*
1723-1724 125

7. *Beyond Time*
1725-1763 139

PART 4: Hour of Seed
Garnet, 1765-1775 155

Miracles 167

Research 183

References 185

Gratitude 189

About the Author 191

AUGURIES

of

THINGS TO COME

Poems & Prose

WORLDWIDE CONSORTIUM OF MUSEUMS

FOR IMMEDIATE RELEASE
Maribel Lagnoth, Director of Outreach
MLagnoth@WWConmuse.org

GUNDESTRUP CAULDRON
REUNITED WITH MISSING PIECE

BRUSSELS, 2 April, 1999 – In a stunning turn of events, the National Museum of Denmark in Copenhagen has announced that the Gundestrup Cauldron is now complete.

The cauldron was found in 1891 by peat diggers in Ravemosen, a bog located near the Danish village of Gundestrup in northern Jutland. The large ceremonial cauldron, dating from the Pre-Roman Iron Age and made from nearly pure silver, appeared to have been ritually buried.

Constructed from a series of exterior and interior plates that fit into a heavy circular base and were anchored at the top by gold rim pieces, the precious vessel had been disassembled before burial took place. The plates and rim pieces were placed neatly into the base.

The five interior plates are embossed with various scenes and symbols, many of Celtic origin and others exhibiting an assortment of animals, including lions, elephants, and mythic gryphons. The seven outer plates depict gods and goddesses, each accompanied by their unique symbology.

3

The craftsmanship that created the cauldron is exceptionally fine and is thought to be Thracian, judging by the techniques used. When experts at the museum reassembled the cauldron after it was found, they determined that it was missing one external plate. Since the existing plates show four gods and three goddesses, it has been widely assumed that the missing piece bears the image of a goddess.

After a century-long absence, the missing plate has been located. It was donated to the National Museum of Denmark in Copenhagen by an American woman who found it among her father's belongings following his death. How the priceless missing piece came into her father's possession is unknown.

On the 1st of June, the complete cauldron will be unveiled at a special ceremony at the museum, after which it will be on public display. Until then, the identity of the missing goddess is being kept secret by museum staff.

Worldwide Consortium of Museums
Rue Vrede 99 • 1047 Brussels, Belgium • WWConmuse.org
Providing Thoughtful Outreach
to Curious Citizens of the World

Part 1
Hour of Smoke

Lena

1997-1998

Listening

When you're the daughter of a man
who was a soldier,
who was captured, imprisoned
    almost unto death,
who walked to freedom
and was sheltered by his
    enemy,
you have to listen,
though he never spoke of it.

So you listen to other things:
    rain on the roof
    and in the gutters, sigh
    and call of wind, his snoring
    on the other side of your bedroom wall
    before you go to sleep.

You spend your childhood
    staring out windows
    at moving clouds, at flickering
    light on the stones of the driveway.

It is up to you to read the signs.
It is up to you to dream your
    dreams.

You come to understand that the land
    holds everything you need
    to know.
And the sky.
And the water.
And you can dream into them.

Her Father's Face

1.

When Lena was a girl, her father's family
bewildered her. People were called aunts
and uncles who weren't related by blood.

Other people, who bore those titles and whose
blood she shared, she saw a few times a year
when her father felt obliged. She could tell

when he did something he'd rather not do.
He fidgeted in his starched shirt and shiny tie.
His face red, he ran his finger under his collar

as if he needed air. That was the way he sat
in church. And on long afternoons visiting
Aunt Enid and Uncle Harold, when the only

sound was the tick of the mantel clock. She'd
sit as still as she could in her ruffled dress,
careful not to kick her patent leather shoes

against the upholstery, waiting the required
time her mother called *polite* before she took
another cookie from the flowery china plate.

Stuck between her parents on the stiff settee
that scratched her calves, she counted the doilies
and the dark, polished floorboards, listening.

2.

Among her father's things, Lena found a photo
labeled on the back with the year his mother
died, 1922, and his name. She'd never seen

an image of him as a boy. He wore a sailor suit
and wide-brimmed hat, a feather tucked
in its band. Though his eyes were shadowed

by the brim, she could see his familiar
features in the little face. He wasn't smiling.

What do I know of my father?

His propensity to laugh, to blast out in anger, to play practical jokes. He turned around and drove in the opposite direction when he saw a black cat. Tossed salt three times over his shoulder when he'd knocked the shaker over, refused to walk under a ladder. Cried on Memorial Day.

I wish I could have known him when he was young, when the world was waiting for him. I wonder what he wished for. Things didn't land in his lap. Some things chose him: his mother's death when he was five, the Great Depression, his halted eighth-grade education, a World War II German prison camp, his faulty heart.

Now I have only this box, this sturdy, worn box half full of things he squirreled away. Among them, a pipe he didn't smoke anymore. A photo of him on his honeymoon, one arm by his side, the other with bent elbow resting on the sign reading, *Danger Keep Away*. His big smile, the pipe held jauntily in his beautiful white teeth. His wedding band on one hand, a flashier ring on the other, blurred in the photo to a glow.

He was a Fifties dad, kept a steady job, was faithful to my mother, worked on the house every weekend, washed the car and mowed the lawn, saved his money, spoiled me.

We used to fight a lot, about things that didn't matter. He'd fought to save the world; I wanted to smash it, make it start over. When I was a girl, he was my idol. When I grew old enough to fight with him, we did.

What did he think about when he'd stare off into space, out the window, his eyes unfocused? How do I find him in this box? I wish I could talk to him now—the things I'd ask him if only I could.

At the bottom of the box, something I've never seen before: a silver rectangle, heavy, ancient, bearing the relief of a fierce woman's face, her hair a mass of coiling, wriggling snakes, her arms raised, a snake coiled around each hand.

Student of Trees

Trees understand wind. Wind understands sky. Sky understands space. Space understands the bits and pieces that make life, since everything is made of stars. I learned this as a little girl, when my family arrived home from a long drive on a starry summer night. As I walked across the yard to the house, I looked up, and in that moment the stars reached down to tell me who I am. My body tingled with the sensation that I was alive. Alive. And I knew that I was given life by an impulse of the overarching canopy of stars.

Ask a tree and you'll know. Trees have special knowledge because they reach into the earth. The tiniest feather of root relays the most sensitive of messages to the tree's substantial heart. And they reach into the sky, receptive day and night to everything that passes. Even young trees gain this knowledge, their roots entwined with the old ones.

You can't argue with trees or tell them something they don't need to hear. Listen to their leaves and needles murmuring in wind. Sit in their high, woven branches and see what they see. Stand tucked into a crevice in a great trunk, or in the space between two companion trees, inhale their changing scents. If you stay long enough, a tree will do its work on you. And if you can't put what you've learned into words, or the words you find are feeble, you still know. As you walk through the woods, the trees will come to know you. It's simple, really.

I can't explain how I came to study trees. I think they must have chosen me, because I didn't set out to learn from them. Many important things in life arrive like maple seeds on their spinning wings. To question or try to explain their origins is to miss the point.

So I spend a part of each day with trees, a few minutes or several hours, listening, touching, looking, breathing, humbled by their vast stores of knowledge, their ancient and far-reaching intelligence. I will never know all they have to teach. But every day gives me a small reckoning of their majesty.

I woke early,

my body fully returned to this world, the dresser and bookcase taking shape out of shadow into soft dawn light.

In broken English, a woman's voice spoke these words: *Every day I dig rocks. If rocks be potatoes, I eat them.*

She went on to describe an encounter that led from rocks to bones to men and tears. I wrote her words down exactly as she'd said them. When she visits, I write her words carefully. If I invite her to speak, she doesn't oblige. She comes when she will.

I've wondered why she chose me. I've wondered how old she is, where she is. None of this wondering does any good. So I walk through the woods, lean against a cedar, sniff the air, watch wind ripple the bay, study clouds.

Lately, I've taken to holding a rock, cradled in the bowl of my cupped hands, a rock I've carried with me wherever I've lived, for the past thirty years. I found it at the base of a pine, upriver from where I was born. It's shaped like a slightly flattened egg, rounded and smoothed by water and stone and sand. It bears dark shiny streaks that look like runes, and a human figure with breasts, mounded belly and wild hair. If I turn the rock, it says different things, the runes tipped or spun into new meanings. I start and end each day in its company.

I am a misfit. The world speaks to me through wind on my face or light moving across the floor. I see things in the dark, and often in daylight, that most people would be certain aren't there. If I think about them, they vanish, so I've learned not to think when they arrive, but only to be open. Eventually, I discover what they want of me.

I'm careful what I say to other people. My way of knowing needs protection. I've trusted too easily, loved too easily, so I've learned to have faith in myself. To trust those who have their own languages: trees, moss, rocks, deer, birds, mist, sky.

Important words I write down in notebooks I keep to myself. They have their own power. The more I write them, the more potent they become.

I've learned that the heart, the bones, muscle and skin have their own libraries. My real job in this world is to uncover all mine have to say, not an easy task. I've been practicing it ever since I can remember, ever since I was five and my body vibrated with star-filled life.

Ever since I heard her voice—

crows follow me, day after day,
when I walk. Night after night,
an owl calls outside my window,
guides me, dreams me, into the dark.

Leaping and running downhill
through the forest—a deer moves
beside me. A strong updraft lifts me
through a blue hole in the treetops.

I gasp for breath. Hawks circle,
guiding with their outstretched wings,
and I soar. The whirlpool of air
carries me upward, higher and higher.

A black bear stands on her hind legs
next to my bed. She's silent, still,
her scent sweet. She wavers, begins
to fade. Before she disappears,
her paw is tender on my forehead.

Thick roots, many-layered, some worn
to bare wood—beneath them, a wolf,
curled up and sleeping. I crouch, peel back

a dense blanket of moss with my left hand.
Coiled in the roots below is a white snake.

A long building woven of saplings
and bark—an old woman invites me
inside, gives me a stone, marbled
gray, studded with bits of quartz.
In its center a deep, purple-red gleam.
The stone fits perfectly in my palm. I
cradle its jagged edges. The woman

feeds me from a great iron kettle, mush
that tastes of corn, warm and filling. She
tells me, not in words, to let my fear go
into the smoke from the fire. I do as she
says, and I rise, up through the smoke hole
into a sky without stars or moon. A huge
dancing figure envelops me in his wings.

I hold the stone against my belly, both hands
cupped over it, and ride waves of fear. My
arms open, press against the great whirling
force, the glowing stone balanced in my
upturned hand. Its brilliance fills the space
around me, until all I can see is light.

Part 2
Hour of Need

Bill

1944-1945

Stand of Birches

Bill wasn't a fighter, though he'd fought along with the rest of them. It hadn't done much good, rifles against artillery and tanks. He watched his feet move, step by step. Sometimes the crusted snow held his weight. More often he sank above his knees into the freezing mass. In the first hours, he'd exchanged glances with the men next to him, but the looks didn't mean anything. There was nothing to say or do.

In boot camp, they didn't prepare you to be a prisoner of war. You didn't practice a forced march under the single eye of a German rifle. You didn't learn how to keep from stumbling, how to keep from being prodded upright by a German bayonet. How to manage the burning thirst that ice made hotter, the sharp hunger that snow couldn't dull. Cold that clawed your skin and sucked the marrow from your bones.

In boot camp, they taught you how to take apart your rifle, clean and load it, find your target. But his rifle was gone. Bill lifted his eyes to the canopy of oak and birch, spruce and pine. They settled him.

His job at the defense plant had let him marry Madeline, start a life with her that he wanted to keep. Grinding steel was the means to do his part and go home to her. When the draft notice finally came, he took a forged hardness to boot camp. If the date of his birth had been a few months earlier, he'd have been too old to serve. He'd still be polishing parts for aircraft engines, and he might have thought steel to be kind.

The job before the defense plant was the one he'd loved: working in the woods. He'd pruned trees, thinned areas where they grew too tightly, gave seedlings the best chance to survive. He'd written *arborist* as his occupation on his induction papers—what he wanted to be. All around the new Barkhamsted Reservoir he'd planted thousands and thousands of seedlings. The fact that they'd be alive long after he was gone had thrilled him.

Each dawn at the reservoir Bill visited a stand of birches on the eastern slope. Golden light crept up their trunks, revealing their bark: rough black strokes against smooth white paper. Those trees had stood for over a hundred years, and he'd wondered what they remembered of those who'd come before him.

Birches possessed a tenderness underlaid by strength and flexibility, qualities he'd longed for. He hadn't known what to do with all the things he felt. A sharp word was enough to make his heart curl like a porcupine, spikes protecting soft underbelly. Birches could withstand snow and ice without snapping. They gave their sweet, pale leaves and smallest black-tipped branches to autumn wind, but in winter they remained whole.

On this first day of his captivity, the valves of the reservoir were opened. Clean, fresh water began its flow all the way to Hartford. The pines and hemlocks he'd planted were taking deeper root, working to hold the banks in place. The stand of birches witnessed the hidden movement of water. Trees had taught Bill how to be a man.

Part 2: Hour of Need

First Night

*The cold can take your limbs or your life, but
not your heart.* The thought seemed
to rise from the ground, from the hollow
free of snow under the pine where Bill had settled.
After the day's forced march, the tree
gave him all it could: warmth
against his back, respite, a bit of sleep.

The German guard was young, not much more
than a boy. The gun he hugged made him
older at first, but Bill could see
in moonlight the raw nerve in his darting eyes,
his bewilderment.

They were the only two awake.
The other guards were beyond Bill's view. The other
prisoners lay strewn across the snow like dark litter
from a harsh wind. He knew
some of them were already lost, would not wake
at the first-light prod of a bayonet.

The boy's pacing brought him closer.
Bill saw a bit of flame, the glow
of the cigarette's tip like a tiny red star.

Please, Bill whispered into the frozen air. The boy
glanced his way, his face set in the hard frown
he'd been trained to bear. He stared,
took a few more steps, his boots
breaking the icy crust.
Bill closed his eyes, waited for the blow.

But the boy squatted down, his back
against the pine's trunk. He took a drag,
then held the cigarette out for Bill.
Each took his time.
Each turn a slow inhale, a long exhale, until
there was just a nub.
The rifle rested on the boy's knees.
He kept one hand on it.

They savored the smoke between them.

The Silence Left Behind

After days without food, after a few men
were shot in the back for trying to sneak
away, the rest grew solitary, isolated,
though they walked in tight formation.

As they passed through a village, gaunt faces
haunted windows like ghosts. Traces of
lives dotted the street: a skinny, frozen dog,
a child's red mitten, a shred of newspaper.

Sometimes the men were kept in a church
overnight, the air murmuring with prayers
and muffled crying until an icy hush invaded
the dark. The guards at the doors didn't sleep.

Sometimes the men were funneled through
narrow lanes to a village square, where they
slept huddled together in groups, leaning in
for warmth, breathing each other's breath.

Sometimes they stumbled through farmland,
held in a cattle pen or pigsty for the night, or
if they were lucky, a barn. One man, his leg
broken when he leapt from the hayloft door

to escape, was shot like a lame horse. And
another, caught trying to milk the single
bony cow, was killed before dawn, the men
awakened by boots pounding his curled body.

Days became one day, nights one night.
Footsteps measured hours and miles. When
rest came, there were no half-smiles, no
meeting eyes. The Germans took everything.

The silence left behind began to talk. Bill
heard a rock's slow speech, the moon's bold
voice, a stream's gentle lilt beneath the snow.

Held Inside

He tried to be angry with the snow.
He knew it threatened to kill him.
Its beautiful silence masked the terrible chill.
Cold gripped his limbs. Icicles glinted
around him, caught in meager sun.

But he couldn't seem to aim his anger there,
couldn't even aim it at the Germans
with their icy guns, who hobbled
through the crusted layers like he did.

He let the anger warm him from inside,
held there like a coal waiting to kindle flame.
It gave him energy to keep going. Maybe
it wasn't anger at all, but a burning drive
to go on living, to survive this endless
march to a place he didn't know the name of.

Bill focused on the snow, how it took its time,
flake by flake, to remake the land. The pines
were magnificent, their branches bowing
under the weight, paying homage to the earth
they grew from. They whispered, shaking
snow from their tips, lifting to receive more.

Birches and oaks, their branches darkened
by thick ice, harbored buds kept safe all winter.
The land hibernated like a great bear, cradled
Bill in its paws, its wide reach toward spring.

Part 3
Hour of Bread

Agnes

1705-1763

1. The Turning

Rhine River Valley
1705-1709

In the fevertime

dreams wandered the land, looking for
those who could see them, who could hear
their incantations, sometimes quiet

and melodious, sometimes raspy and harsh.
They spoke from the land, from the waters
and trees, from rock cliffs and wide sky.

Most of the village denied them, called them
delirium, the workings of evil or punishment,
turning their backs, covering their ears,

and pleading with the God they feared.
But Oma welcomed the visions, the voices,
kept all their prophecies. She let them

reverberate inside her, through her flesh
and bones and blood. And they returned
ever after, as Oma taught Agnes how to

find them, at twilight or dawn when they
visited, in winter silence, at the edges
of forest or river, under the crescent moon.

Along the Rhine

Among men, words traveled along the river,
words they grasped in their calloused hands,
mulled with their wine over the fire. They tossed
them from hand to hand, their mouths forming
words around words, heads shaking or nodding
together. Most of the women swallowed
this talk, followed speech mumbled in sleep
or under the breath, in their baskets caught
tones hurled into wind and scattered like seed.

It was different for some women—a very few.
What passed downstream among them was
silent: an herb to seat a baby in the womb,
leaves to ease fever sores, a root to halt a baby
and return monthly blood. Once in a while
a braid of straw and hair, its strands signaling
witchery, warning the one next to be accused.

Agnes kept watch by the river, read its changing
banks, its riffles and swells, listened to its liquid
speech and icy groans. She knew its great power
to carry words that altered the men and nearly all
of the women, their doings made strange by anger
and fear, by righteousness, their faces unmasked.

Oma said to hold fast, like the trees that reached
their tendrils to drink, all the way from the forest.
Like rock that parted the waters, gentled the current.

How Women Called Forth the Moon

Long ago, when the land grew dark and silent,
people were blind and had to feel their way.
There were no moon or stars then, night a fist

holding tight to everything. High in a great oak,
as the sun slipped from sight, a man hung
a lamp he'd bought from a stranger. The rest

of the men were pleased that night, for they
could see freely. Soon other men wanted one,
and the trees bent under the strain of all

the hanging globes. Each day they climbed
to fill their lamps with the stranger's oil,
and each night they roamed as they wished.

But then there was no oil left, dark returned
and the stranger was gone. They took down
the lamps, cursing them, casting them aside.

After the women heard their words, they stole
into the night, gathered the shards, buried them
in earth as dark as sky, trusting in the work

of their hands. At dawn, from where the shards
lay deep in the soil, green shoots emerged,
grew all that day and bloomed. That night,

a bright orb rose overhead. In its light the land
was made wide, visible. The next night
the same thing happened, and all the nights

following. To speak their thanks, the women
named the orb *Moon*. And to this day,
it is why women plant when the moon is full.

Queen Anne's Golden Book

Agnes had learned to be a listener early. Just
as her grandmother schooled her in the Ways
of the Mother, so she'd taught Agnes about

the ways of men. Wayward and slanted, things
in the world made by men had no sense to them.
Oma could look at the moon's face and predict

when snow would come, but the visage of a man
did not tell what he might do. Oma did not believe
that God had a plan, but the Mother had Her signs

and Her seasons, spoke aloud in wind and sun.
At times, She kept to Herself, withheld the rains
or rendered the air painfully chill. *She have Her*

reasons, Oma would say. *The scales of men be*
ever tipped, but Her scale of seasons always
be balanced. At night around the hearth, the men

shared news that traveled the Rhine, the flames
snapping punctuation. The emptying wine jars
and punishing work had loosened their tongues.

The Prince's portion be too high, one complained.
Yea, my part be less and less, agreed another, *bare*
enough to feed the babes, and a new one on the way.

Soon we earn naught for ourselves. Then Johann
joined in, *Tis worse for us who rents the land.*
The Prince own us, body and labor, and the food

in our mouths belong to him. Above the grumbling
and unnamable fear a new voice arose, a tinker
from the Lahn River Valley who had stopped

for the night. *I hear Queen Anne of England deed
land to those who go to America, and passage
to get there.* Just then the fire gave a sharp crack,

tossed onto the hearth a bright, sparkling ember.
*A man from my village hear it read from a book
bearing the Queen's likeness and bound all in gold.*

The Turning

1. Winter

The sky was a weary color. Cold clutched
the land. Sun begrudged its meager light,
barely announcing the day. Cracks shattered
the silence as branches split from frozen
trunks and fell. The small circle of heat
from the fire was everything. No choice

but to wake in the night and tend the fire,
to wake in the morning and tend the fire,
hungrier than any babe. Even the heat
of lying with Johann gave little comfort.
Agnes faced the hours with ordinary
courage, without energy to rouse more.

Then the wind arrived, overtaking all
other sound, as if soldiers pounded
toward them, horses unreined and cannons
relentless. It swept down the wide valley
in waves, shaking the door, lifting the roof.
A volley of air snuffed the fire, like a candle

blown out by a breath. Then the wind ended,
leaving behind something more terrible
than the litter of fruit trees and grapevines,
ripped from the ground, strewn like chaff.

2. Spring

Agnes could hear tiny rivulets trickling
under the snow, and the ice that gripped
the river yawned and stretched. Day by day,
the snow withered and the river ice groaned,
heaving itself in chunks from the water.
As soon as they could enter the forest, Agnes

and her grandmother sought the Sacred Oak.
Tis standing! Oma said. *We must give thanks.*
Fingers of sun reached through its branches,
lending warmth to the buds at their tips.
Agnes and Oma did not speak of devastation,
of broken orchards and shredded vines,

of the harvest ruined for years to come.
Instead, they offered the first ceremony
of spring. *Praise be to Oak, to sweet soil.*
Agnes started the song, joined by Oma
as they lifted their arms and danced.
In spite of the harshest winter in memory

and the fiercest of winds that had ever
visited the valley. These were the forces
of the Mother. They must honor Her Ways.

3. Night

Around the communal fire, the men spoke
of nothing else: *There be no harvest. Yet*
we must pay tax and tithe just the same. Aye,
and naught for paying. Sheep and cows
all frozen or starved. The women huddled
together, traded ways to stretch what was left:

Sawdust in the flour be more filling than
plain. Bones bear more broth after prayer.
At first, they fed orphans and old ones,
along with those too weak to work. *This be*
worse than the plagues, grumbled a man
one night by the fire. *Hush*, said another,

today be the first with no funeral. Ye ought
to give thanks to the Lord. Last season's
last jar of wine loosened talk around
the circle. When it ran out, there was quiet.
Oma poked at the embers with a stick,
added a gnarled log, and the flames leapt

and snapped, gave rise to showers of sparks,
stained everyone's faces an eerie red.
In the weeks after, something changed
in the village. Old and weak folk were
neglected. Orphans passed from house
to house unfed. Flour was hoarded, seeds

hidden. Shared fires ceased. Furtive eyes
exchanged glances, whispers grew.

4. Day

After their third spring ceremony, the one
to bless the seeds, Agnes wove her way home
through trees thinned by winter and wind.
Oma stayed behind to hide their work. *Ye must
do everything to live, my Agnes, to keep
the Old Ways*. Oma's parting words unsettled

her, and Agnes kept glancing back. Ahead, she
sensed muffled voices, strange thumps. Wary,
Agnes hid behind a tree, straining to listen.
They were coming closer. *She be drinking
the Devil's milk, keeping her plump all winter
while we starved.* A man's voice, familiar.

*Aye, and we all of us see that night what she
done to the fire.* Another villager began
a hymn, her voice a thin, sharp blade. Agnes
knew then what she had to do, but she could not
move. She could not do what would shatter
her heart. The group passed by, banging

their clubs against the trees in rhythm
with the ponderous hymn they had joined.
Agnes heard again Oma's words, as if
they took shelter inside her, summoning
her arms and legs. *Ye must live.* And she ran.
Not toward her grandmother, but away.

Visit to the Otherworld

Agnes stood with the Sacred Oak, her stance
weighty and deliberate. She studied the fine
patterns of its bark, felt the solid ground

beneath her bare feet. Roots fixed the soil
where she stood. She sensed their reach, wide
and deep, their intermingling with other roots

that formed the forest, their spread weaving
the roof of the Otherworld. It was time to go.
When the earth opened to receive her, descent

was slow and darkness whole. She traveled
as a tendril would, feeling her way with fingers
no longer flesh. The transit was frightening,

but Agnes gave in to it, her mind and heart
no longer hers. The silence was complete,
welcoming, absorbing. There was no time,

no breath, no light, yet she could see. She met
the forces that impelled the realm above. Some
took form and others were formless. All rain

that had ever fallen, all days and nights were
held here, in this place without time or human
sense, in this place that was not a place. Agnes,

no longer Agnes, met the Great Snakes who
twined the roots of the Tree that was Life. There
were seven, their names unspoken, their voices

gentle and full. They told of their grandmother,
she who circled and cradled the earth. They
told of their sister, she who rippled through air

to create the wind. And their cousin, who guarded
rivers and springs. They told her how all things
were brought into being, how the dead and dying

were remade and reborn, how everything rose
from the earth below into the world above, freely
given, how Great Mother birthed it all. When

she returned to the land of breath and light
and hours, Agnes would not remember what
she'd seen and heard, but she would know it.

She would care for the knowing and for the self
that knew. And in that way, no matter how
it seemed on the surface of time, all was well.

Legacy

Ye be one of the keepers now, Oma had told
her when she'd shown Agnes the precious piece
of silver, then tucked it under sheltering roots
of the Oak, where it vanished from sight.

Be fourteen in all, she'd said. *One safe day,
all be gathered again.* Until then, for time
beyond reckoning, keepers held their places
in secret, even from each other, except
to pass the knowledge to a new generation.

Before sleep, Agnes saw Snake Woman, Her
gleaming face embossed on the silver plate, Her
hair long thick snakes, Her hands held out
to earth and sky. Snakes circled Her breasts.

Before sleep, Agnes heard Oma's words. *Healing,
hearth, birth, waters. Of all powers, She be most.*

When she'd fled, Agnes had to leave the plate
behind, but she didn't lose faith. She had done
what her grandmother asked: she had lived.

Snake Woman would find Her way home.
The Sacred Cauldron would be whole again.

Into Time Agnes Dreamed Him

He would walk this land in snow and live. The trees
would bend to shelter him. What he would not know
would not matter. Whether meager sun, whether ice
or moonless night, he would walk this land and live.

He would love trees, their limbs, their crowns, roots
holding them fast. The oak would give him sturdiness,
the birch suppleness, the fir a sense of proportion,
the beech balance. In them he would recognize his kin.

He would have a ready laugh, tender heart, bright eyes.
He would work with his hands. He would go to war.
He would hide his wedding ring under his tongue
to keep it from his captors. He would walk this land

and live. The land he would not know would know him.
His boots cracking through crusted snow would wake
the forest. He would sit in a hollow beneath this oak,
rest his back against its stout trunk. He would sleep,

though cold would sink around him. He would dream
of her who'd dreamed him, understand what he would
not remember. Night shadows would hover around him,
he would lose all fear. He would walk this land and live.

He would dream of her who'd dreamed him, know
beyond forgetting. He would walk this land of meager
food and meager sun and he would live. His bones
would ache with cold and he would wake. Dawn

would come and he would see. He would reach for what he did not know, toward what the oak had saved. He would walk this land and live. He would reach among the roots. His hands would find the treasure.

2. Night and Day at Sea

Aboard Ship
1710

Auguries of Things to Come

When Agnes dreamed, she dreamed
about the ship. In daylight she didn't like
to remember it, but at night it swallowed her,
like one of the monsters from the old stories,

groaning and belching. On calm days
during the voyage, the ship creaked
and swayed, a giant mother carrying her
and all the others, great hands of water

resting against its rough belly.
But during much of the endless trip,
it was tossed about like a pebble
from hand to hand, and she with it,

a tiny speck of flint. In the beginning
birds followed overhead, and she
could read their wings and the soft
undersides of their bellies, auguries

that spoke of things to come.
Her grandmother had taught her how
to separate herself from what she saw,
so that what she saw did not become

laden with her. For three days the birds
followed the ship, their dark wings
writing on the sky. She read them
each day, keeping their messages

to herself as the women of her line
had instructed, generation after generation.
There were seven birds, all the same kind
though different from each other. One

called more than the rest, but none of them
were silent. They were birds she didn't know,
just as she didn't know the sea. Still,
she knew that these birds had something

to tell her. She would hold their secrets
until she understood them, until they ripened
like berries hidden in the forest, slowly
sweetening. She would wait for the right

moment to harvest, their flavors revealed
suddenly on her tongue. But overnight
the birds disappeared, changing the sky
to a vast nothing. It was difficult to know

what to do without the earth beneath her,
the good rich dirt. Once, the oldest oak
had told her, *the cycles are long*. She did not
know how to read the sea, but she would learn.

Night and Day at Sea

1.

On a night when she longed most for home,
Agnes stood on deck with the moon. She
wondered if the moon conversed with the sea,
for the water was dyed with its light.
Or if the sea kept her secrets to herself.

On a day when there were sheep's wool clouds,
Agnes visited her home that was no longer.
Hidden near the stern, out of the wind, she
could hear Oma's voice, see the Sacred Oak
and the worlds beneath. And she wept.

Aye, good luck! Agnes traced the odd words
to a sailor leaning against the rail. She rose
shakily to her feet, looked where he pointed.
There was wool on the water, as if clouds
had fallen and unwound, trailing the ship.

Sea beings broke through, silvery and fast,
leaping, diving, skimming the water's rippled skin.
Gut, Agnes said in her own tongue, but the sailor
was gone. "*Gut*," she said again, her heart soaring.
It was the first time the sea had spoken to her.

2.

Agnes held fast to the ways she knew, even
on the changeable sea. In the morning she
consecrated herself to the sun, and at night
she aligned with the moon and stars. Between,
in all the hours, she kept two selves, the one
the others thought was she, and the hidden one.

As a girl, she'd mastered well the six-days
duties her mother required—baking, tending,
stitching, scrubbing, milking, weeding,
stewing—and on the Sabbath she'd churched
faithfully, mouthed hymns and prayers
in the mask that Oma taught her to bear.

On the ship it was harder to keep the Old Ways,
crowded among ears poised to listen and gazes
that followed. Agnes hallowed the place
at the stern where the sea had first spoken,
sending the sailor and the bringers of luck.
Her prayers made certain the Old Ways lived.

3.

An enormous being rose from the foam, blowing
a burst from the top of its head. One of the sailors
shouted, *Whale!* waving his cap, his hair whipping
in the wind. Johann laughed at his antics, and Agnes
smiled to see him laugh. Mirth had been a stranger

ever since they'd fled, since the weeks-long journey
down the Rhine, the stark months in Rotterdam
and London, the cruel, starved waiting for the ship.
The leviathan arched, its body glowing red-gold
in the sunset, its tail slicing the water. Then it dove,

taking all the dark memories into the deep. Johann
kissed her, an unchaste kiss, right there on the deck.
What think ye of, now, on this night? Johann asked.
Agnes could feel the warmth of his arm against hers.
Of the day ye asked for my hand. That be a good day.

Through the sleeve of his jacket and the wool
of her shawl, she could feel the heat. *Aye, that be
a good day. Let us go below*, Johann said. Agnes
thanked the sun as it flamed its last light, as it slipped
beneath the far line where sky and sea knew each other.

Storm

Wind took the ship in its jaws, shook it
in jagged teeth. Ocean's hooked talons
held it aloft, then dropped it, a mere twig.
Agnes hoped the trees of its making

remembered their courage and strength.
She touched Johann's cheek, traced
the line of his jaw, felt its clench. There was
no speaking above the roar, so she kept

her hand on his face, his hand reaching
to cover hers. No one ate, and sleep
never came. There was no going on deck,
no peace, no air. The sharp smell of fear

added to the loathsome stink below, where
everyone kept to their berths, held on. But
Agnes possessed the force of remembrance:
Let us pay homage to the trees, Oma had said

on the bright morning after a terrible storm.
They'd crossed the soaked meadow, Agnes's
small hand inside her grandmother's,
and entered the forest. Branches, thicker

than Oma's legs, were strewn everywhere.
Tears wet Agnes's cheeks, but she wiped them
on her sleeve and kept going, scrambling
over the storm's waste. When they came upon

two great downed trees, Agnes collapsed
into sobs. One had been ripped from its roots,
and in its falling had broken the other. They
lay side by side, fractured. *Ye must not grieve*

for them, Oma whispered, wrapping Agnes
in her arms. *They give themselves to warm us
in winters to come, give their branches to feed
new trees.* Agnes breathed the earthen scents,

and her tears ebbed into the silence. *This be
the forest's way, and the way of the wind. Come,
let us go on.* When they arrived at the Sacred Oak,
it stood as majestic as always, its roots holding

deep into the Otherworld, its branches aimed far
into sky. Oma placed her left palm on the bark,
and Agnes placed her right. Joining hands
between them, they made a circle with the Oak.

Praise be, Oma had said. Agnes wished
she could tell Johann this story. With one hand
in his and the other on the wood of the ship,
she created a circle of prayer, flesh to flesh.

Ocean Sacrifice

The sea blossomed with flowers, its great skin
ornamented by white buds that burst open, faded,
renewed, and faded again. Its growing season was
quick, its liquid fields fertile and ever changing.

Agnes knew there must be a force that was Ocean,
just as there was She who was Land. As the ship
set sail, Agnes had seen where they met and wished
she could have lingered there, where the two greeted
each other, to straddle them and sense their powers.

Yet now she knew that the sea she'd never met before
was revelation. It was enough to ride upon Her
in the tiny ship and learn Her ways. For endless weeks
Her fearsome aspect had seized the ship—so huge
in the harbor—and made it small. But in these flowers
She showed Her gentle side, and Agnes was thankful.

For three days of blossoms, Agnes made offerings
over the rail: a knot of her hair, a bit of yarn,
three precious seeds. They were borne away by wind,
swallowed by swells. Agnes did not know any ocean
prayers, so she gave sky prayers to the faraway
line where they met. *Sky must speak to Sea, just as
She always be talking with Land,* she thought.

But the following morning the buds were sheared off
by a sideways wind before they could bloom, and
by mid-day the sky grew dark. Those were the hours
of the first deaths, a newborn boy and his mother.

Using all that Oma had taught her, Agnes caught the baby. But she knew right away that he'd come too soon and would not live. Agnes saw that there was too much blood, and even with her strong tea of lady's mantle and shepherd's purse, the mother followed the boy before she could name him.

That evening the two bodies were given to the sea, wrapped together in the bloody blanket, along with stones from the bowels of the ship. The captain spoke words in his tongue, and a minister from the mother's village spoke more, his voice sharpened by God's wrath. Agnes bowed her head and closed her eyes.

She thought of the first day out, when ocean beings had followed the ship as it left the harbor, followed into open water. They had dark, shining heads, and their nostrils flared with their breaths. When they dove, their bodies were slippery and sleek.

One had risen very near the ship, gazed at Agnes with its round, sweet eyes. She wondered where those spirits were now as she whispered, *Amen.*

St. Elmo's Fire

Just as the ship trusted the sea, Agnes knew the moon
was there. Clouds had gathered to commune with it
in private. This was the night
                    to offer thanksgiving
                                    for the child.

When her moonbleed time had passed without a sign
of sacred blood, Agnes had ached for Oma. Too soon
for forceful herbs, she'd made a tea of chamomile
and meadowsweet. In the scent rising from the cup
she'd let her worries lift: how to seat the babe, how
to blossom it, with food and water scant.
                    Oma was with her
                                    still.

On deck, Agnes beheld a far-off blade of light
that cut the heavy fleece of cloud, and distant
pounding answered it. She entered their communion,
in the stir of hairs at the back of her neck, in the shiver
that ran along her spine. Spirits crowded around,
all due her thanks, those who had come before,
those not yet arrived.
                    A potent night to make
                                    an offering.

Closer now, another streaking blade, another
rejoining rumble, the clouds soon rioting
with celebration. From the tips of the masts
blue snakes danced, hissing to her far below.
When Agnes raised her hand in greeting, sparks
flew from her fingertips. She lifted her arms,
fingers spread wide, hands wild with vibration,
with crackling light. As if she
                        were the living fuel
                                    for fire.

Full Moon

Agnes always had stars, even aboard the ship.
With only hewn planks beneath and no earth
to hold her, she could rely on the moon, its glow
magnified over blank water. Night after night,

she braced herself against the rail, marveling
at unobstructed sky. She asked the moon
to guide her as it had always done, witnessing
its pregnant girth, keeping vigil until she could
hear its fullest voice. On nights when wind
was too fierce or clouds too thick, Agnes

stayed below and dreamed. Dreams allowed
passage between worlds, between the one she
could feel with her fingers and Others, where
she did not need hands and feet or breath and eyes.
Doors opened if the moment was correct, the need

distinct. On this round lunar night, the ship
pitched so badly that Agnes could not stand,
so she lay below, wrapped in her grandmother's
shawl. Oma had spun the yarn by moonlight
and completed the weaving between full moons.

As a girl, Agnes sat by the loom, watching
Oma's fingers move in nimble rhythm, as wool
gave itself over and sang. When Agnes reached
her first moonblood, Oma gave the shawl to her,
spoke of ancient times in the women's hut, where
they'd assembled each month in their potency.

Grandmothers held their own circles, initiated
the girls-become-women, gathered the ritual
blood. The men brought them food, performed
all the women's tasks during their seclusion.
The sacred hut had long ago decayed, plowed
under to make a new field. But only brambles

grew there ever after. Those were just a few
of the stories Oma had told. It was dangerous
to speak of the Old Ways. Even Agnes's mother
could not know, since she was devout in the way
that erased everything, devout in the way
Oma and Agnes pretended to be. On this night

aboard ship, the shawl brought Oma to Agnes,
and with her came the songs for dreaming. The sky
was clear in the Otherworld, where the sky always
lived. Agnes watched the stars as they traveled,
as the animals that were the stars revealed themselves.

Immense wildcats lit the darkness with majesty. One
rested on its haunches, one lifted its huge paw, and one
roamed widely, flicking its bushy, black-ringed tail.
Lynx—greatest cat of all—crouched, readying itself
to run. And when it ran, its radiance streaked across

the sky. Just as quickly, the view was overtaken
by a pair of gigantic wings, as an owl rose, the moon
far behind it. The owl was bright white, with random
black markings. It was Moon Owl, flying silently
until it encircled the moon in enormous wings, until
Moon and Owl became one, a bird made of light.

3. *Arrival*

Schoharie Valley
British Colonial New York
1712-1714

How Schoharie Valley Was Made

The land gave and the land received.
It had always been the way: the land's
generosity and that of the waters and sky.

In a place before time, water knew to form
ice, with help from sky and land. Ice knew
its path, scouring a valley where a valley

had not been. Rock knew to give itself
to ice, to give way, just as ice came to know
its return to water, thundering down

the valley. The land knew there would be those
to come, come into time, those who would know
and keep. The land saw their traces, sensed them.

Long before time, the land waited.

Every day I dig rocks.

If rocks be potatoes, I eat them.
I make line, pile stones, weeks-long fence.
Field have shape.

Men come.
Tall men, deep eyes, hold themselves up.
Johann don't like them.
But I see their eyes, something they know.

I dig rocks all day, many, many days.
Yesterday I find bones.

Today I show tall men bones.
They speak together.
One talk to me, I not understand.
But his eyes cry and his voice be soft.

I give him my shawl.
He lay it on dug earth.
With words he gather bones.
Wrap bones inside my cloth, sing soft.

He hold bones like they be baby, carry them away.
My eyes on his back.

Great Oak, New Land

People come from oak, Agnes
said aloud, wishing for Oma's

voice. *Snakes live under roots.*
Leaves cling, drop, make way

for man catkins, woman buds.
In the forest she'd discovered

a stand of oak. The oldest one
beckoned her. She touched

rough bark shaped like thumbs,
spread her hands against

the thickness, pressed
skin to skin. Fingers

of sun reached down, warm.
Each morning she would

come here to worship.
In a cleft Agnes placed

a rock from the Old Land,
white, shaped like a dove.

Winter Gifts at Schoharie Creek

After the hardships, many of the others called this valley
harsh and unwilling. But Agnes saw its kindness. She
did not pray to the land the way others prayed to God,
pleading for forgiveness or vengeance, two far points

that could never meet. The land was not fickle like God.
The first winter brought piercing cold, snow up to the hips,
wind that shook the little cabin she and Johann had built.
They hoped their meager provisions would last, the small

yield Agnes had coaxed from the rough plot she'd cleared
by hand. She'd acquired a nanny goat and a ewe, payment
for attending some of the women in secret or spinning wool
for those wealthy enough for a shearing. Late in the season,

she and Johann had gathered a cutting of hay. They would
keep the two animals alive for as long as they could, aimed
toward spring breeding. Though they never spoke of
their prospects, they knew all their hopes were thin.

> *We have good luck*, Agnes would say.
> *Goat and sheep and hay warm us this winter.*

> *I am glad for this potato*, Johann would answer.
> *Thanks be to God.*

> *Yea, this potato be from land*, Agnes would add.
> *Thanks be to Land.*

And they'd smile.
These were the conversations they preferred.

Then gifts appeared outside the cabin, just after the first
deep snow. There were four puzzling bentwood
frames laced with hide strips, sturdy and carefully made.
A few mornings later Agnes woke to a soft, shuffling

sound. Pushing open the door, she saw fresh meat laid
just outside, and a woman walking away on the snow
as if it were solid ground. Clad in leather and fur,
she wore the same wooden frames strapped to her feet.

> *Thanks be!* Agnes called.
> And the woman turned.

> She was Sarah, granddaughter of the old ones
> who had sold them their land.

> *Thanks be!* Agnes called again.
> And Sarah laughed.

> *I know ye!* Agnes shouted, waving wildly.
> Sarah laughed again, notes sweeter than birdsong.

First Spring at Prayer Creek

The creek broke upon her like dawn. First came
its sound, calling before Agnes had even arrived,
rushing like wind through the valley. Close enough
to see it, she could feel its power vibrate the ground.

She had walked nearly three hours north
from the makeshift cabin to discover this place.
All forces of the land were here—rock, water,
trees, the noblest three. And above—sky,
where rain and night and lightning dwelled.

Agnes knew this place would tell her its name.
There was no other sound but its voice, rising
beyond the forest. She followed the water's surge
as it descended to the Schoharie, its fury a wonder.

Stowing her bonnet, her shoes and stockings
into the roots of a maple, Agnes tucked her skirt
into her belt. She climbed over slick stones,
over trees that had given themselves to the creek.
Her steps were certain, her whole body a prayer.
She knew how to live as a prayer, as Oma had lived.

By a pool below a waterfall, Agnes bathed her feet
in its coolness, her tears mingling with its welcome.
At times, on the arduous journey to this land, fear
had engulfed her—in the vast cities of Rotterdam
and London and New York. In the quaking ship
on relentless seas, where so many had perished.

And in the grueling labor forced by the British,
harvesting pine sap to make tar for their ships.
But when the creek told her its name, Agnes knew
that three years of hardship had been worth the price.
She would make a new life, deepen the Old Ways.

Downstream, she stopped where the creek slowed
over a broad arc of stairs it carved from the shale.
On the first shelf down from the crest lay
a white rattlesnake, well over thirty feet long,
extending from one bank to the other, its head
facing Agnes. Its body undulated in the flowing
water, beautiful patterns wavering on its back.

Agnes looked into its watchful eyes and saw
it was the creek's guardian, telling her no harm
would come to this place. Sunlight and shadow
danced over their faces, and the snake disappeared.

Arrival

Sarah be friend. I never have friend before, only myself for talking, Agnes thought, on her way to Sarah's cabin. She hummed one of Oma's songs, a song for Snake Woman, who blessed

the waters and rains. Without Her, there was no life. It had been so long since Agnes could speak with Oma about the things that mattered. Silence made them potent, yet silence was lonely.

Agnes gave many of her thoughts to the cows' udders and the soil, to the sheep's wool and her loom. They conversed with her in their own languages, filling her days with communion. Yet the good fortune

that arrived in Sarah was far beyond anything Agnes had known. Sarah was always glad to see her. Theirs was a friendship of eyes and gentle nods, of noticings exchanged. Of cooking pots ready to share. Agnes

knew Sarah's real name, but she used the one given by the missionary, even when they were alone. Oma had taught her protection of power, the risk of diminishment from too much talk. Agnes's

basket held two loaves of bread and a chunk of fresh butter. She never went to Sarah's cabin empty handed, for without Sarah and her family, she and Johann would have no farm. The land was everything, and theirs had belonged to Sarah's people for generations beyond count. They'd sold them enough to make a good farm, a solid agreement made with honor and good will and writ on paper. Without their generosity, Agnes

and Johann would not have survived their first winter. Sarah's mother and grandmother had become Agnes's own. She walked with light steps in rhythm with Oma's song. At the edge of Sarah's land, Agnes called out

the customary greeting. Sunlight sparkled in her eyes. The day's chores were done, and she had a few spare hours before milking, time for her friend. Sarah's voice called out in answer, and her laugh invited Agnes in.

Drought

Day after day, sun roasted
the land. Shadows were few

and the earth lay naked, its skin
dry and burning. Agnes visited

the Great Oak, placed offerings
at its base, where roots passed

into the ground. Oak knew all
about water, about forces deep

underneath and high above
that conjoined to make rain.

Oak knew what to do, how to
ask. Agnes knew only to pray.

Voices of the Land

Green mountains on both sides of the valley stretched as far as Agnes could see. They watched over ripening fields and the moving river that made its way north. The eastern ridge held morning sun, then released its warmth to the valley. At day's end, its mate to the west pulled the sun down, and the valley shadowed and cooled. Sarah told her that far to the south were more mountains, where the river began. Agnes wondered about that place.

When the sun went to the Otherworld, the twin ridges guarded the valley. Sun had business to attend to before it returned unencumbered each morning. Others did not note its passing, except as it ordered the labor of their farms. Moon's daytime work was shrouded in the Otherworld.

Scattered in the mountains were bare rock cliffs, absorbing light throughout night and day, one reason why rock knew so much. Sometimes a cliff split open, birthing children whose clamor echoed down the valley.

Soil met rain, held what was buried, both shallow and deep. Each morning Agnes cupped a handful, and its knowing passed into her palm. She picked up a pebble, whose knowledge was slow to impart to her skin. And she placed them back where they belonged.

Rain's many voices were meant for the land. Others discussed it incessantly, but Agnes preferred to accept what it chose: to wash the earth gently or wash it away, depending on what soil asked.

Wind spoke into the chimney, its cries mournful, insistent, amused, or angry, visiting often because Agnes listened. Outside her door, its breath left sticks or a bird's nest or circle of leaves. She read them where they lay, then carried them to the Great Oak.

Lightning left singe and fire, its speech quick. Because it could seek out a person for death, others feared it. Thunder's voice shook everything in the valley while jagged streaks enlivened the sky. Agnes studied them well.

Gentle in summer, silent in winter, wild in spring, the river's voice was endless. It was called Schoharie Creek, after uprooted trees that rushed downstream to form dams and change its course. Men had taken the name from Sarah's people, though they did not understand its meaning or hear correctly the word they took. To the north, it flowed into a river called Mohawk. Agnes had never been there, though she saw it in dreams.

When it flooded, the river spread silt and stones and remnants of trees, offerings it made to the land. Agnes gathered bits of these gifts in an earthen bowl, careful not to take too much. She set the bowl beneath the Oak, where she contemplated their meanings.

At the turn of each season, Agnes sought Prayer Creek, its meanderings and waterfalls and the place where it joined the Schoharie. Always, it offered a balm and a blessing. Always, it received her gifts. Prayer Creek and Agnes kept faith with each other.

Message from Prayer Creek

A piece of wood floated in an eddy, in rhythm
as the water flexed. Too regular to be fashioned
by the Mother, it seemed the craft of human hands.

Agnes considered the work of the Mother:
gentle and knowing trees, rocks that held the soil
in place. And water, so clear and changeable.

In the New Land, the Mother cared for Agnes
as She had always done. Even in Her harshness,
in storm and ice, the Mother never failed.

Agnes remembered the work of human hands:
the silver plate she'd had to leave behind, where
Oma had buried it, under the Sacred Oak's root.

She knew that even so far away, the Oak
could sense her thoughts, just as the maples
surrounding her now could hear her prayers.

Agnes waded across to see what the creek offered:
a spoon, its bowl round, perfect for scooping mush
or stirring soup, bringing goodness to someone's lips.

At the handle's tip was the image of a bear, its fierce
kindness. She saw the carver seated in the fire's glow
in darkest winter, all contained in the ancient wood.

By moonlight she took the gift to Sarah's grandmother.
I know ye be her clan. As she spoke those words,
Agnes understood what the bear had come to tell her.

When the time was right, the hidden silver plate
would reveal itself. The Oak, the earth, the Mother
would give protection until it found the way home.

Healing Johann

1.

Johann had not fared well during the British time near the river called Hudson. He had never been an angry man, yet he grew angry then.

The land had been stingy, the soil poor and full of sand. Agnes tried to make a garden on the tiny plot she'd been assigned, but it yielded little, and the rationed food was scant. She didn't like to remember it now, in this green valley with its wide river called Schoharie Creek. Here the land was generous and kind.

The men had tried to refuse the forest work. What did farmers know about making pine tar for British ships? Where was the land they'd been promised? The answer from the British lord who owned their labor was to cut their rations. Their debt was ever-growing, the cost of their food and supplies added to the price of their passage. *Those times liken to a bad well*, thought Agnes. *The deeper dug, the more foul the water be.*

Worst of all had been the months when the governor took the men away, made them walk north behind British soldiers to rout the soldiers of the French. The men had food for the journey, but the women left behind were given nothing. They ground tree bark into flour, boiled bits of hay to make bitter soup, watched their little ones fail one by one. All the while, the British lady in her fine house refused them bread. She lavished meals on her children—tender lamb and sweet puddings—and bade her servants throw the scraps to fatten the pigs.

When the mission failed, British soldiers returned with the men, forcing them back to the forest, guarding their daily labor. The only good to come of it had been meeting the warriors called Haudenosaunee, who'd walked north along with them. The warriors were upright in their dealings, skilled at the hunt, knew the vast land they traveled.

The men's resistance finally won out, the forest work abandoned. Three years after they'd fled the Rhine, Agnes and Johann and a group of the others arrived in the valley called Schoharie. Agnes gave thanks each morning to the soil. *The dark earth go deep*, she thought. *The soil liken to a clear, clean spring, never-failing.*

Yet Johann still had uneasy days, when his words were few and his smile thin. Agnes wondered if the British lord still pecked at him, like a woodpecker after grubs in a tree no longer sound.

2.

One night the moon bore an eerie countenance, reddening and disappearing, as if the shadow of a great hand passed over its face, blinding its eyes bit by bit, rendering the land completely dark. Agnes wondered at this sign. She waited, her heart pounding, her breath shallow. She watched as the shadow-hand held the moon, then remade it, piece by piece.

The next morning she sought her friend Sarah. She brought a gift of fresh tallow and an embroidered handkerchief she'd made during the winter from a scrap of shirt. Sarah received the gifts with open hands as was her way. She offered Agnes a bowl of corn stew, and they ate together. Sarah's pot was always full.

I be need gut kraft for Johann, Agnes said. *I fear he still be lost in British forest. Moon show me in the night.*

Sarah took a dried plant from one earthen jar and a tall cluster of dried blossoms from another. She put a cup of water into a small iron pot and brought it to a boil on the fire, then poured it over the herbs, singing quietly as she worked.

Agnes recognized the first plant as Self-Heal. She knew the second plant as Mother's Lip, for the shape of its buds and its red color. Oma had refused to use the plant's common name—Cardinal Flower—for the robes of the high Roman priests. *Nay, she be named for the mouth of the Mother,* Oma had insisted.

As Agnes and Sarah waited for the liquid to cool, each smiled in her separate thoughts. Talk diluted medicine's power, a truth their grandmothers had taught. They were used to sharing silence.

Drink all at once were Sarah's few words, as she drained the cool tea into a cup. Agnes found Johann resting under a tree at the edge of the field. *I be some awful tired*, Johann said, his face sunken.

Be drinking this down. Ye have lost heart, Agnes said. He wiped his forehead on his sleeve and accepted the cup, making a terrible face as he gulped the liquid. All night he was sick. Each time he vomited, Agnes went outside to look at the moon—at its full and shining face.

In the morning Johann kept down water, and at noon he showed an appetite for the corn stew Sarah brought them. Later he ate a hearty dinner. By nightfall, his smile lit the room as brightly as the moonlight streaming through the window.

Spring Sign

In the New Land, Agnes rose well before Johann each day.
> Facing east, she knelt and kissed the earth, her time
> with the Mother spent in silence. One spring morning
> a doe emerged from the forest's edge, passing so close

their breaths mixed in the air. The beginnings of birdsong
> lilted like water bubbling over stones. In the mirrors
> of the doe's dark eyes, she saw her own twinned
> reflections. Agnes did not speak. Animals preferred

their own languages. Hearing a hatchling beg to be fed
> and a duckling peep for its mother, she recalled
> long days on the ship when she lay becalmed, to save
> the babe in her womb. A dark-eyed woman tended her

with potent teas and ancient words. But the babe could not
> stay. With the woman by her side, Agnes performed
> a private burial, dropping the bloody bundle over
> the rail, nothing to weight it but grief. Agnes watched

the small roll of cloth float away, until it disappeared.
> When she turned, the woman was gone. Agnes
> searched for her in the days that followed, to offer
> a token of thanks. But she wasn't to be found.

As the doe moved on, she looked back at Agnes, bending
> her slender neck as if to show the swell of her belly.
> Agnes understood what the doe had come to say.
> *No moonblood*, she realized. *Doe tell me true.*

Inside the cabin Agnes stoked the fire, rousing Johann from the last of his sleep. When she spoke her news, Johann's smile set his eyes alight. *Thanks be to God,* he said. *Thanks be to the Mother,* she whispered.

Night Keepers

The others spoke of them with fearsome words, as if
     the noises of darkness were curses or slanders
     put forth by the land. Yet the beings of the dark
     did their nightly work. Agnes knew this to be true.

Oma had taught her the symmetry of opposites, of moon
     and sun, winter and summer, east and west, of all
     partnered forces woven together to make the world.

She recounted old tales of wolves with the power of speech
     and she-bears who mothered lost children. *The men
     fear them needless*, she would say. *They know not
     their protection. Wolf and Bear be keepers of night.*

Oma's eyes shone with remembrance, as she told the story
     of the girl who lost her way in the forest at day's end.
     Her basket of berries was heavy, and she stumbled
     over rock and root. The air grew chill and dank.

*Then a she-bear come and wrap her in her arms, same
     as I hold ye now*, Oma said, *and she slept warm
     all the night. She-Bear guard children, always.*

In the New Land, the others could abide neither darkness
     nor forest. But Agnes bid welcome to both,
     as vital as luminous day and neatly tilled field.

The singing of wolves was a comfort. *If they take a sheep,
     it be needful*, she thought. But it did no good
     to speak of it. The minds of the others were hard.

On washing day, at the edge of the creek, she came upon
bear tracks glistening in the mud. Agnes placed
a small water-worn stone in each of the prints,
for the little babe who was growing inside her.

Want and Plenty

To touch the earth with her hands, with her feet, with her eyes was prayer. Others would name it *pride* and *vanity*, but Agnes called it worship.

In the night an owl cried out, inviting her to remember the simplest and truest thing: there was always balance. Night and day, fall and spring, want and plenty, death and birth. She'd learned to love them equally.

Others cursed drought and flood, declared they arrived as punishment. They summoned each other to atone. They named the soft rain *good*, the bright sun *good*, and they spoke as if they must earn them, the goods of living.

But the owl's clear tones were a reminder. There was no scale for weighing worth or lack. Was a lamb better than a rock, or a man better than a woman? It could not be so, for there was only endless life.

Agnes wished to tell the others to give up sin. It was just a thought to organize their fear. But their ears were attuned to harshness, and their hearts hardened by need. So she kept her peace, kept the Old Ways, alone.

The Mother's Ways were many but simple. They could not be understood, only lived. Agnes's eyes were the Mother's eyes, her ears the Mother's ears. Her skin was the Mother's, and her heart.

Earth and Water

There were greens in this valley
that she'd dreamed of.
Sprouting corn and squash,
flowering willow and birch
conspired to feed her eyes.

She held her first living babe,
a daughter of the earth.
Agnes knew that her womb
and the hills were no different.

This babe was also of the water,
arrived in a flood, birthed
from all the waters
that fed the valley.
As the river spilled its banks,
she'd flowed from Agnes's body.

If her daughter should die,
Agnes would plant her in the soil,
and something new
would grow from her.
Agnes would mourn her flesh
and love what grew.

If she should live,
the Old Ways would live on.
Her tiny hands reached into the air,
and her eyes were open.

4. *Good Days*

1714-1715

Snow's Embrace

When snow coated
the tender land, all who lived underneath shared
their secrets. Stones spoke to dirt. Fish and turtles
spoke under ice. None were overheard.

Agnes lingered
midway to the barn, breathing snow's clean
fragrance, listening to silence. Nearly dawn,
rose-gold light touched the treetops.

Trees were slow
in winter, sleeping in the cold, holding fast
against wind. In the barn, Agnes rubbed the cow's
belly. *Ye be calving in spring.*

She remembered
last year's blizzard, the oneness of white erasing
earth and sky. Ice claws clung to the roof edge.
Drifts climbed halfway up the windows. Johann
was nearly lost between barn and house, when
the guide rope gave way in his hand.

Just then, Agnes
held a lamp at the top of the window. Just then,
Johann saw it. Afterwards, she told him,
I had a notion. When he could breathe again,
when his mouth could form words, he replied,
Blessed be your notions.

                    Snow was gentle
when it wished, when protection and healing
were needed beneath: after drought, after flood,
after people made roads where earth did not
want them.

                    Sky and earth
mated in snow, their children birthed in spring,
countless as stars—all the furred and scaled
and feathered beings, the many-legged
and buzzing ones, all the buds and sap, rock,
tendrils of vines, seedlings, mushrooms,
water, mud, moss.

At the Loom

There was the yarn—the strong warp and supple
      weft, becoming something beyond themselves
      to gentle the cold.

There was the lamb, who arrived in slippery blood,
      stood to suckle on wobbly legs, scampered
      over the fields. And his mother, wrapped
      in her thick coat that gave way to the shears.

There was the new, raw wool combed and combed,
      washed in the river, dried in soft breeze.

There was the clean roving, spun and plied,
      the pedal moving in quiet rhythm, the wheel
      whirring a steady hum.

There was the oak, its roots reaching down and deep
      into earth, its branches up and wide into sky.
      The oak gave itself to the saw, for the wheel
      to spin the wool and the loom to weave it.

There were the plants, born from cracks in their seeds
      to carve their blind way through soil, to rise
      into sun and rain, to make roots and leaves,
      nuts and flowers and fruits. They yielded
      to the pestle, joined with water, changed
      wool into rainbows.

There were the ancestors, lingering in Agnes's bones.
Her fingers and eyes, devoted to the yarn, held
the long line of women who came before.

There was the blanket emerging on the loom, colors
forming patterns, patterns telling stories, stories
speaking truths that came from the Mother,
returned to the Mother, came again.

Wind and Water

Along the miles to Prayer Creek, Agnes's
eyes feasted on opening buds and currents
of moving clouds. At the first waterfall,
she perched on a rock shelf and breathed

the braided scents of soil, water, tree. Twined
with all those around her, large, small, seen,
unseen. Nothing to ask for, only to praise.
Prayer Creek spoke in its own way, tumbling

toward the greater waters of the creek called
Schoharie, the river called Mohawk, the river
called Hudson, and into the ocean that Agnes
had crossed in the little wooden ship. How tiny

were the ways of men, mere splinters floating
on endless water, sailing by a whim of wind.

Nightwalk

The trails of night were secret, open
only to eyes and ears attuned to darkness,
to footsteps that barely grazed the ground,
gliding over roots and rocks. Agnes did not
know where she was going. The forces
        of daylight slept,
          there was nothing to pursue.

The forest arched over her. Sky arched
over the forest, stars and moon
        and realms beyond them,
        farther still.

Beneath her was earth and all below, snaking
tendrils and the waters they drank from,
seed, soil, egg, larvae, burrow, stone, worm,
        all the moist and gritty realms,
        deeper still.

Agnes was held within, where sky joined
earth, great worlds above and below.
She walked in the direction of their meeting,
yet knew she would never arrive.
Their union was not a place, sky and land
        stitched together,
        without seam or thread,
        end or beginning.

Owl's Cry

Odd to hear Owl call so late in the morning.
Be gift of vision, Agnes thought, closing her eyes
while she churned the thickening cream,
the rhythm of her arms and hands transporting her.

To her left, a stir in the air, something soft
like a child's hand brushing her arm—
and she knew what was asking to be seen.

Agnes ran. The butter would spoil, but no matter.
She knew what was at stake. Owl cried again,
as she sped across the new-seeded field to the trees.
Johann paused his plow, but Agnes did not stop.

Her sides began to hurt, but she pushed through
the stitches of pain. *Sarah!* she screamed with all
the breath she had, pounding on her friend's door.

Sure-footed as deer, the two women descended
into the draw beyond the cabin, splashed through
the shallow stream, climbed to the uphill woodlands,
to reach Sarah's son, the boy named for wandering.

He was unconscious, his leg caught in an iron trap.
Agnes tore her smock, held it against the gaping
wound, while Sarah pried open the terrible jaws.

The women tended him all night. Sarah's mother
sang as she brewed fresh medicine—compresses
of sassafras leaves in white pine needle tea.
In the haze before dawn, Agnes sensed Oma near.

When sunlight cleared the eastern ridge, Agnes
grew certain the boy would live. She hastened back
to fetch the trap, tucked it away in the root cellar.

At sunrise on Sunday she stole to Becker's barn,
the makeshift place of worship until a proper church
was built. She laid the thing at the top of the stairs
that rose to the minister's rough-hewn pulpit.

There would be no need to speak of righteousness
in boundary lines. The trespassing trap and the little
boy's blood would deliver a sermon of their own.

Handiwork

Hands do not measure time. Nor anything
to do with thought. They read the warmth
of the sun on newly turned soil, the fever
of skin, the softening of ice. They know when

the stones of the oven are right for the dough,
when the ewe is ready to lamb, the cow
overdue for milking, the corn ripe and sweet.
Hands built the road to this place—finally—

of arrival, hands split and raw. Hands are
eyes in the dark, sensing shifts in the wind,
remembering the bark of every tree. They
understand the suppleness of hides, the fine

softness of petals. Hands ease newborns into breath,
enliven the needle that whispers through cloth.
Hands bundle the hay, bathe the dead and bury them.
They shear thick wool, wash it clean of dried dung

and mud, collect its oils to mix into salve, pick out
its burrs and bugs and sticks, then comb it. They spin
plied yarn, gather flowers, roots and nuts for dyes,
weave the blanket and make the mattress it covers.

Hands attend the woman who is sick or dull, heavy
with child, frightened or starving, dispossessed,
downcast, or mad. Sometimes hands, too tender
for this world, retreat under the folds of a shawl.

Those are the times when they know too much, when they cannot unknow. Yet when they are called, hands return to their tasks. When they are called, they give offerings, open their palms to sky.

Good Days

Agnes stood at the threshold and looked out
over the land, the good, sweet land. Her heart
felt sweet and good just to look at it. *Yea,*
the land have a soul, she thought, *a broad,*

dark soul. It know to grow stout trees
from tender sprouts. There was nothing
a tree could not do, standing through flood
and drought, offering itself to become

useful things: buckets and wheels, plows
and churns. A cradle. Mortar and pestle.
A door. She knew her house to be wise,
its frame, floors and ceiling built from

the wisest oak. Inside, its walls finished
with mud, made from earth, from all earth
knew of seasons. She hoped the house
would hold her forever in this place

she had come to love, a love that had no
end, like the spring that gave fresh water
day after day. Even if she lived to be
an old woman with wild white hair, she

knew she could never, not even then, know
more bounty than she already had, here
where she stood on a fine morning when clouds
laced the sun. Thresholds were for knowing

future and past, for pausing between, where
there was nothing but a new day, full
of hard, good work. Agnes was blessed
by her days, one after the other, blessed by

what her days and the land gave: everything.
A prayer rose to her lips, a prayer of thanksgiving
to the earth that never failed her. She lingered
on the threshold to feel it, then stepped over.

Midwife's Song

Babes come to the womb from the Otherworld.
Quickening is the sign they may choose
the path here. Babes are uncertain. They look
forward, look back. Meadow chickweed guides
the way, beech bark or prickly ash eases return.

Birthing is jagged and sharp, surges of water
and blood over cliffs, a final plunge to the river.
Sometimes a babe cannot stay, the time not
auspicious, the Otherworld's pull too strong.

A sun child is born of buzz and shadow, a moon
child of stillness and fox cry. Children are made
by seasons and storms. Creek, rock, glint of mica
and ice do their part. A dusk babe is born
of smoke, a dawn babe of birdwings and mist.

Mothering is a bowl, a spindle, fertile soil
freshly plowed. Over weeks, even months,
babes remain distant, not yet fully arrived.
You can see the Otherworld in their eyes, feel
it in their skin, smell it in their hair. Breasts hold
the flow to this life, coaxing them all the way in.

Children are fashioned by snakeskin and spider.
By breeze, lightning, drought, dust. Birch, flood
and bloom. We cannot read who they are. If we
keep careful watch, they allow us to know
them. They will give themselves to this world.

Moon Birth

Agnes longed for a daughter, one to learn the Old Ways, to continue her line. Johann hoped for a son, for company in barn and fields, his new line in the New Land. This Agnes understood. Though Johann accepted her ways, he was one of the others.

Agnes could feel restive movements, the baby's eagerness to arrive. *Be the eyes open or closed,* she wondered.

The land warmed, welcoming plow and planting. The ewes would lamb and the cows would calf. Agnes rubbed their swollen bellies for luck, touched their soft noses, smelled their sweet breath. Boy or girl, if this baby lived, it would be enough.

She'd already lost three. The unformed one on the ship, who'd ended in blood and was given to the sea. The tiny boy who'd come too early, and the girl born in flood, whose life slipped away after the waters receded. Those two lay buried uphill from the house. Johann marked their graves with crosses. Agnes marked their passing with two stone circles, hidden on the far side of Prayer Creek.

But this one would live. Sarah and her mother and grandmother sang over it, taught Agnes which plants to gather and how to prepare them, shared from their most potent stores. The baby's stirrings, from the beginning, were strong. *Whoever ye be, ye be welcome,* Agnes said each day when she woke, each night before sleep. Johann smiled at her words.

One morning she rose early, stole from the house while Johann slept. The moon still glowed above the western ridge. Agnes felt the baby's weight, closed her eyes, drank the moonlight in. *Babe be wash by Moon*, she whispered.

Her spine tingled. The air bore a powerful scent of earth. Agnes opened her eyes to a bear, a sow with a mewling cub. They were nearly close enough to touch. The mother reared to standing, her hind legs like tree trunks, her front paws reaching toward Agnes. Their eyes met in greeting.

Praise be to thee. Thanks be, Agnes said, as the sow went on her way, her fat cub following.

The next night Agnes birthed a living son. Johann fetched Sarah and her mother and grandmother as Agnes asked. They provided an easy birth.

Johann gave the boy his Christian name, *Hermanus*. To Agnes, he would always be *Agate*, a gem she knew from the Old Land.

To her, he would always be the boy who gleamed in a she-bear's eyes.

5. The Land Speaks

1722

Wind Dancer

Wind shivered the windows, shuddered the roof.
Agnes lay still, wishing to answer it, but she
did not know its question, nor what it foretold.

A figure appeared, a man made from shadow,
from a charcoal darkness deeper than the air.
He was bent at the waist, folded over the hollow

at the center of his body. Slowly, inch by inch,
he straightened. His great wings opened, spread
wide as the room. He danced, his feet light

on the floor, barely touching, his wings beating
as silently as an owl's, in rhythm with the waves
of wind rolling through the valley. He moved

closer and closer, took Agnes into his wings,
into the darkest darkness she had ever known.
She couldn't keep still, her body raw with fear,

writhing, as the wings consumed her completely.
Agnes closed her eyes, slipped into the narrow
passage between worlds, entered the boundless

cavern of the Mother's womb, where there was
help beyond asking, vision beyond eyes, sensing
beyond body, knowledge beyond mind, trust.

There Agnes would understand her place. In dawn
light, the dancer was gone, leaving a purple glow,
a wavering outline of where he had been.

Ordinary Days

1. On the First Day Following the Wind

Agnes stoked the fire to heat the stone walls of the oven, built into the chimney next to the fireplace. The wide raised hearth held enough warmth to proof dough, keep stew hot, and from its place in the center of the house, nurture life. Fire possessed the power to transform: grain into bread, game into stew.

Agnes tested the oven by reaching inside to feel the right temperature for bread. Later, as the oven cooled a bit, she'd put in the pies made from last fall's apples, she'd bake them long and slow. Though it was grueling, hot work, Agnes never failed to thank the fire.

One day we have outdoors oven, Johann said when they took their midday meal outside in the shade. Agnes tried to smile as she took off her sodden bonnet. Wisps of wet hair clung to her face and neck.

Aye, that be good, she said between gulps of water. The heat took her appetite, so she gave her piece of warm bread to Johann. She glanced at the far ridge that bordered one side of their valley, at the greening trees that climbed its steep slope. Spring allowed her to say that she could stretch the flour no farther. *But there be corn meal still.*

Corn meal be fine, answered Johann. Basking in his ready smile, Agnes looked toward the house and barn. They stood strong and bold against the bright sky, anchored to their own piece of land. She still marveled at how far they'd come to find it, the farm they'd built in eight years' time. The cabin of their first winter looked so tiny now.

Agate be home soon, Agnes said. They lent him each season to the Weiser farm—to help with the chores and be schooled to read and write. *He be our hopes*, she added, easing his absence.

That evening, Agnes cut into one of the pies and lifted a steaming slice onto one of the wooden plates Johann made during the winter, its border a wreath of carved flowers. She fed him a bite from her spoon, and he fed her in turn from his, as if they were robins ready to nest, and then used their fingers to gather the juice. When the plate was clean, they kissed, savoring the sweetness.

Before dark, Agnes took the best of the pies to her friend Sarah. There would be no apples without Sarah's orchard. There would be no corn if Sarah had not taught them how to grow it. There would be no farm if Sarah's elders had not sold them good land. There would be no life at all, if Sarah and her family had not seen them through their first winter, through their whole first year.

2. On the Second Day After the Wind

Agnes used sand from the creek's edge, along with her soap, to rub stains from their few clothes and linens. She took great care with them, her scrubbing gentle and patient. She spread the clean laundry over the rocks on shore to dry in the sun. Lingering by the creek, she cupped her rough, chafed hands in the water and lifted them, letting it run through her fingers. *Praise be*, Agnes said, as the surface sparkled and rainbows formed in the air.

After their midday meal, Johann returned to plowing a newly cleared field and Agnes gathered the dried laundry. *Mattress need tending*, Agnes thought on her way back to the house. She hauled it outside, bound it with sturdy rope and dragged it to the edge of the field where Johann worked. He would chop the matted straw apart, spread it over the soil after the seeds were sown.

Now that the last of the snow had finally gone, they could spare straw from the barn. Agnes tied it into bundles and laced them together, relishing the treat of new beds, of sheets and blankets fresh with spring sun, and Agate's return.

3. On the Third Day

Agnes and Johann planted the new field for their first crop of wheat. The night before, Agnes planted seeds in the four corners of the field under the full moon. As she had done in the Old Land, so she did in the New. *Each seed be prayer*, Agnes said.

There were so many things to praise. The kindness of Sarah's family. The charity of strangers in the early years who'd sent food from the city called New York. And those in Rotterdam and London who did not forsake them to perish in the camps, awaiting Queen Anne to pronounce their fate. The Old Land that grew them. The New Land that saved them.

News Arrives

1.

Agnes walked the miles from Prayer Creek
absorbed in lilting birdsong, golden light,
cool, spring-scented air. Approaching home,
she saw Johann pacing back and forth
between house and barn. As she called out,
he hastened to meet her, swiping at his tears.

Not Agate, she faltered, but he managed
to shake his head. She led him into the house,
to the chair by the hearth, busied herself
with stew she'd left simmering that morning.
Thanks be to Sarah for the meat, she said softly.
Her uncle made a fine hunt. Perhaps her simple
prayer would lift Johann enough to speak.

He sank with each word of his news, as if muscle
had forsaken bone and could not uphold him.
*The big men in Albany writ we must leave
this valley. They say our land not owned legal.*

2.

My hands be empty, Agnes said as Sarah invited
her in. *I bring ye my trouble.* Sarah served her
an ample helping of corn mush. Agnes ate slowly.
She had no appetite, but it would not do to refuse
the gift. Sarah's baby boy played at their feet
with a little collection of sticks and rocks.

*The lordly men in Albany writ we cannot own
our land.* As Agnes spoke, Sarah nodded slowly,
as if puzzling out each word, letter by letter.

Ye buy it legal from the elders, Sarah answered,
eyes flashing. *We have paper marked and signed.*

Thanks be for ye, great friend, Agnes whispered,
unleashing her tears into the afternoon's heart.
The baby looked at Agnes, then at his mother,
at the glistening tracks that appeared on Sarah's
face. He began to babble his own kind of song.

While the women cried, he continued to sing.
Gradually, he grew louder, more boisterous,
until there was no room any longer for sorrow.

Aftermath

For most of the night, Agnes lay awake. Johann woke at times, startled by dreams, but he seemed not to know her when she offered comfort. There was no moon, nor any stars. The sky wore a mask as dark as Agnes had ever seen. She hoped for a sign, but there was none.

If sorrow meant ownership, they'd paid more than their share. The babe they'd lost on the ship, two babes buried on the rise behind the house. Every beloved person and sacred place they'd left behind in the Old Land.

If toil meant ownership, they'd paid many times over. They'd cleared stubborn rocks to make fields. Built a strong barn and proud house. Shepherded their animals, wasted nothing of their milk and wool and flesh and bones. They'd plowed and planted, harvested and put by for winter. All with their own hands.

If gifts meant ownership, they'd received plenty. A healthy son. Rich soil as deep as the walls of their house were tall. The broad valley flanked by high ridges. The wide creek that never failed. Trees that gave themselves for building and warmth, for fences and tools. Woodlands that offered berries, healing plants, meat. The kindness of friends—Sarah and her family—who'd taught them how to live.

The land did not doubt Agnes's rightful place.

Stir of Words

Ever since Johann had brought home the news,
nights seemed longer, yet dawn came earlier.
Agnes knew how to be with seasons and weather,

but the ways of men were impossible to follow.
Through lingering drought and ferocious flood,
she had never once thought of leaving the farm.

A crow lay stiff outside the door, its claws
curled. Agnes placed the body under the Oak,
covered with a cairn of flat stones she'd gathered

by the river. That night when she lay down, she
could still see the lifeless eyes. They took
away her sleep, cast her into a dreamless dark.

Some of the others had already gone. Agnes
could not face it, starting again when this place
was all she'd dreamed of. What it had taken

to get here—starvation and cold, the endless,
bitter voyage, harsh toil under cruel British
soldiers, the first two winters of ice and lack—

all of it filled a feeble measure compared
to this land. At first, Johann's eyes blazed
and his words flamed. He and the other men

stirred pots of talk, stoked the fires that roared
beneath. They would fight. They would prevail.
But the Big Men in faraway Albany were not

swayed by an X on a bit of paper, nor by threats.
The men were ants beneath their feet. A new
look appeared in Johann's eyes, a golden gleam

that lit up his countenance and remained.
His words softened, yet made her more afraid.
They say the land up north be better than this

and rightfully ours writ on papers, he'd say.
Agnes would answer, *Speak not of this*,
but it did not stop him, each of his words

a smoldering ember. *The land be greener*
and more of it. The river be bigger and fine.
Words, spoken and unspoken, troubled her days.

The Land Speaks

Clouds moved in, dark and low, erasing
the ridgetops, then settling into the valley.
Agnes could barely see beyond the creek,
the air a thick gray mist. She couldn't help
smiling, despite the worries that troubled her.
Thanks be to clouds and waters of the air.

The men had gathered, more than twoscore,
nearly all the men from the valley. It was not
their way to fight. Yet they had suffered
to arrive here. They would not suffer leaving.

We must be buying our land all over again,
from Big Men in Albany, or be gone from it,
Johann said. He looked smaller of stature, his face
pinched. *I be listening to the men. Some say fight.*
Some say go. Some say buy again. Some say wait.

For Agnes, the question was different from those
the men asked, the choice of action more obscure.
She wondered what the land wanted them to do.

That evening, Johan stirred the fire, brightening
the room. Agnes used a twig to ignite a candle
for more light, settled with her sewing. She closed
her eyes to give a prayer of thanks, and the glow
transformed from purple to green, then blue.
The ancestors be shining in me, she thought.

In the middle of the night, Agnes woke
to thrumming on the roof. The noise intensified.
She slipped from bed, cracked the door open.
Even in darkness, she could see the coating
of white on the ground, hailstones bouncing
as they hit, accumulating quickly. She
made her way back to bed. Johann did not stir.

Agnes lay awake, and the hail kept drumming.
In the distance, the cry of a night-bird arose,
one she'd never heard before, sounding again
and again, clear and bold, and the hail became
a deluge of rain. The bird stopped calling then.

The downpour continued through the next day,
and for three days following. Lightning tore
at the ridges. The creek churned with mud,
clawing at its edges, but the land held fast.

Owl's View

After Albany Big Men cast ruin over the small, after Johann's face turned waxen and Agate's anger mute, Agnes sought the Great Oak. She often went during the high-sun meal, while Johann and Agate picked at their food. On days when all her hours were spent with work—on laundry day or baking day—she made her visit after dark. Her feet knew the way, and gradually her eyes could follow.

Darkness held a different kind of quiet than day. All the night beings, spirit or flesh, moved slowly and softly, and the sounds they made were secretive. Openings to the Otherworld grew wider, and beings of the dark moved easily between.

Night belonged to owl, fox, lynx, wolf, bobcat, coyote, cougar and bear. To spirits of pale, shimmering light and dense, weighty shadow. Some night spirits danced. Some stilled themselves in crevices. Others rearranged what had been done in daylight. Trees and rocks sometimes walked about, sometimes slept.

One night when restlessness had overtaken the house, when Johann and Agate wrestled with sleep, Agnes slipped away. At the edge of the forest, an owl waited, then accompanied her on noiseless wings. Her pace was careful and deliberate, and the owl alighted several times until she caught up. Once they reached the Great Oak, the owl perched on the lowest branch and greeted Agnes with its eyes.

Owl was a being of silence and seeing, and to meet its eyes was to accept an invitation. Owl's head tilted this way and that. Its wings stretched and fluttered, then settled again.

And Agnes flew with Owl's wings and looked with Owl's eyes. She saw Owl's view of the farm, of Sarah's cabin, of woods and fields and river, of all the miles to Prayer Creek, shining under the moon. The starry, whirling sky surrounded her with wakefulness.

Gently, Owl returned her to the ground, set her down beneath the Oak's stout limbs. It was then that Agnes knew what she would do. She knew where she belonged. She was rooted here, as solid as the Oak, as sure as forest and field and the garden she tended.

No matter the ways of men, big or small, she would stay.

6. Then and Now

1723-1724

Absence

For a long while, the world was hollow.
Sounds echoed fiercely before they
disappeared. Agnes's broom swishing
across the floor could nearly set
the timbers rumbling. And when
the broom stopped, the silence was
almost more than Agnes could bear.

For weeks before the leaving, Johann
had been tender, his eyes fluid and shining.
He spoke little, and when he did, his words
wavered. *I cannot leave ye*, he would say,
or *Ye must come. The land there be as good.*
Sometimes a single word, *Please.*

The parting had been stern, Johann's face
holding none of its former softness.
Shaking his head, he implored her, *I cannot
understand ye*, his only words. Agnes had
thought he'd meant to say more, but he did not.

Small part man, large part still boy, Agate
rubbed at his eyes with his sleeve. He hugged
Agnes to him tightly, let her go without a word.

The line Johann and Agate joined stretched
along the road as far as Agnes could see, a chain
of wagons loaded with sundry implements,
furniture, seed and flour sacks, children
and a year's worth of trembling hope.

The dust they raised soon obliterated them,
leaving only their noise. Then that, too, was gone.

Night Visitors

Agnes's eyes knew the dark,
but there was nothing to see.
These visitors had no shape or form.
Their sounds were soft and insistent,
like melt trickling under snow.
Her heart quickened, yet Oma had
taught her there was nothing to fear.
And so it was not fear she felt,
but her body enlivened in welcome.

These beings had no names, no places.
Agnes sensed they were small
and numerous. Their voices were
like whispers, like sighs, but
the language they made was not
words. Their breaths, like tiny fingers,
stroked the air. Agnes's breathing
mingled with theirs until one breath
emerged, strong and sweet.

A glow like honey surrounded her,
and then they departed, leaving her full
of golden light. Agnes drifted into sleep
and dreamed of her babe, fat and new.
She dreamed of her girlchild, named
and growing. When Agnes woke, threads
of sun were weaving themselves into dawn.
She knew then that one of the visitors
had chosen. Her babe would live.

Then and Now

1.

Agnes thought she heard her grandmother's voice, so soft she wondered if she'd imagined it. She strained to listen, then noticed a fineness of light at the edges of things, a glow that reached toward her, revealing what was hidden in the night.

No matter how terrible everything appears, Oma said, *trust.* The flickering light trembled and faded, but the words remained.

Agnes had known it would be hard in this New Land, alone among people who'd lost the Old Ways, who made her business theirs, watching, demanding public confession on their sabbath. They sat upright on their benches, the men on the right side and the women on the left, waiting until someone rose to speak self-chastising words. Each took a turn, the men first, the women following.

Every Sunday Agnes offered believable sins, something amiss but not dire, nothing that would bring too much attention. She'd let the last bit of milk go sour. She'd wished for rain when God had seen fit to bestow endless sun. She'd coveted her neighbor's ample store of flour. Confession was fraught with jeopardy, but silence would mark her just as Oma had been marked.

Agnes was careful to remember the winter before she and Johann had fled. Her bones had been etched by ice, first aching, then burning, then failing her, though she still had to rise each morning. Animals froze to death in the barns. Deer collapsed in open fields. Birds dropped from the sky. Trees split and fell. She was careful to remember that winter's aftermath: Oma accused, blamed, hunted down in the forest.

Woman be witch. Agnes knew it was thought among the others, if not said aloud. She talked of Oma only to Sarah, in rare moments to Johann. She kept her rituals small and hidden and quiet.

2.

Now the farms in the valley were empty, save for Agnes and the animals that Johann had left her: a cow, a calf, a rooster, a dozen chickens and a remnant flock of sheep. In his silence, he had been generous.

Now each thing she did was sacred, as women's work in the Old Time had been. In one long rhythm, she gathered eggs, scattered seed, spun yarn, transformed rich cream into butter. And the land held it all, in its ways of storm and sun, wind and snow, moon and stars. Each day and each night she wove a long ceremony. She sang and prayed aloud, freely visited the Great Oak and Prayer Creek, offered large and joyful thanksgiving.

Now she carried the seedling babe inside her, the one Oma had told her would come, the one who would survive. The one who would learn the Old Ways, let them live.

When Hard Met Hard

1.

Pestle met leaf, comb met raw wool.
Soft yielded to hard, releasing
what was hidden inside:
a tincture, a shawl.

Together, they created what would not be
if they did not meet.
Comb and pestle provided force,
and force was needed for invention.

The babe inside her was soft,
so a hard thing Agnes would be.
And the babe would become its own
tincture and shawl.

This be the way things work. Soil give way
to plow, hay to fork, tree to axe.
Yet Agnes also knew the opposite truth.

Earth and stone give way to water, iron to fire.
She would yield to the babe
at its birth.

2.

The long hand of Albany still reached
toward the farm, hammer in its grip.
But Agnes would give a new telling
to the story of the way things worked:
Hard be meeting hard.

Like flint against rock, she'd make
a spark, revealing
beneath flame and ash what was harder still
and would not yield.

Agnes would be a hard thing for the land.
No matter what the Big Men decreed,
she would not give up her farm.

After and Before

Agnes had always noticed leavings, used
them in all the ways she could. Corn husks.

Frayed rope. Lamb bones. Bits of yarn.
Leavings had their own beauty. Peeling

bark. Calf afterbirth. Last leaves before
snow. Stones at field's edge. Shimmering

mud after rainstorm. Other beauties,
unseen, were no less potent. Bud beneath

thick frost. The moment cream consented
to butter. Silence after Johann and Agate

had gone. Deep of night. The urge to weep.
Agnes had also noticed stirrings, met them

with a glad heart. Birdsong in January thaw.
Ripple of insect or fish on water. Bubble

before boil in the pot. Flour finding rise
to bread. Flutter in her womb, its promise.

The She-Fox

Sadness fell around Agnes like leaves, as she
roamed the woods. Without the others, without
Johann and Agate, there was no one to attend.
Still, she needed medicine to rebuild her stores:
for all the months of winter, for her pregnancy,
for the birth and beyond, for herself and the babe.

The day was dark, the sky gray and gathered
unto itself. At the edge of the marsh, Agnes cut
a share of jewelweed. Their leaves still held the
green of summer, though autumn was showing
its many faces. Bent over her work, she didn't
notice the fox. Then Agnes caught her scent.

Careful not to look her in the eyes, Agnes gazed
off to the side, slowly squatting, making herself
as compact as the she-fox. Under the spell of her
thick red fur, her glorious tail, her small, sweet
head, Agnes understood she was no longer alone.

A few days later she sought Sarah, with a new
winter blanket she'd just finished weaving. Sarah's
cabin was filled with the fragrance of drying herbs,
of fresh fish, and corn stew simmering on the fire.
Agnes sat gratefully on a bench by the window,
her womb growing fuller with the babe each day.
Sarah was the first to break their silence.

A fox came by a few days ago. She spoke
softly, but I could make out her sense.

I, too, met a fox, Agnes offered. *She*
did not speak, but opened my heart.

That is speech just the same. She gave
me a warning, said I must tell you.

Agnes waited, her body sagging with heaviness,
while Sarah took time to find the right words.

They will come, Agnes. They will take
your farm. They will not let you stay.

I know, Agnes said, her voice a whisper.

You are welcome here. You belong here.
You must prepare to move in with us soon,
if not before the snow, then at first thaw.

Agnes had no words in reply. In the glow of Sarah's
hearth, she smiled. Sarah nodded, smiled back.

Garnet's Birth

When Garnet came, Agnes knew she would
live. She came on a night when the moon was
not yet full, and throughout the nights following
she grew as strong as the moon grew round.

Agnes was tended by four generations:
Sarah, her daughter, her mother, her grandmother.
Agnes knew that Oma was there, too, inside

the murmuring of shadows. Even her mother came,
not bound by dogma or desire, a pure presence
like light or water. And there were others Agnes
did not know by name, old, powerful and kind.

When Garnet came, it was a clear night, stars
shimmering in the parts of the sky that the moon
left free. A warm, graceful wind touched the deep
quiet. The ridges guarded the valley, and the river

rippled silver and black. Owls swept silently
through trees, over fields. Cows and sheep
bedded down undisturbed. In the distance, wolf
and bear communed. All the signs were at work

for a good birth, for a long life, for welcome.
Outside the cabin, Sarah's uncle, brother,
and son tended the fire. Inside the cabin,
the women sang the songs of birth and Agnes

prayed. Garnet did her part, too, readied
herself to follow the moon into this world.

7. Beyond Time

1725-1763

The Last Night

Lightning struck the northern ridge, lit
the whole valley, a portent so strong
Agnes knew this would be the last night
at her farm. Garnet slept on, her small body

heavy with dreams. In the flash, Agnes
glimpsed her face, the baby-becoming-girl
curves of her cheeks and chin. Then darkness.
Their new cabin was finished, everything

moved, ready. But Agnes kept wanting to sleep
at the farm, to wake there until the right day
to begin. Gathering clouds hid the moon,
weakened the stars, spoke to the echoing house.

Agnes would make certain no trace of her life
there remained, nothing for strangers to sully.
In the morning she would do a proper ceremony
to free herself and Garnet, to close the door.

She'd never again see the sky from this window.
With family now as much theirs as Sarah's,
she and Garnet would make a good life.
There would be no phantom lines drawn

on shared land. It was the family's way,
no matter the burden, to welcome, to give.
Agnes stood at the window through the storm's
steady coming, its thunder and pounding rain

lingering over the far ridge, its single strike.
As it moved on, slowly quieting, moon and stars
returned with all their shine. A new beginning,
clean and dazzling, was written across the sky.

Making Things Right

Agnes and Sarah sat together, sharing a cup
of water. The two women were silent. Garnet
was nestled between them, drifting into sleep,
as the noises of day gave way to those of night.

Something be heavy with you, Agnes finally said.
    Grandfather saw storms of dust at your farm.
So they come now, to take it.
    Yes. Sarah's word lingered like fever.

The home Agnes had belonged to. The land
of Sarah's ancestors, all the way back to when
Skywoman fell. Sarah and Agnes watched
the moon rise, holding their beginnings.

The next morning Sarah's uncle brought Agnes
a bundle, laid it gently on the ground at her feet.
His eyes filled, and his words were halting:
As you did long ago, I made things right.

Agnes knelt and slowly unfolded the cloth,
a shawl belonging to Sarah's grandmother.
Inside were two small bundles, swathed alike
in softest deerskin. Sarah's uncle knelt down

beside her and began to sing. Agnes's hands
trembled as she unwrapped the deerskin.
Inside were two sets of tiny human bones.
In turn, she held each little skull in her palms.

Then Sarah, her mother and grandmother came
to help Agnes rewrap her lost babies and bury them.
The three women sang over the new place, over
Agnes's bent head and the small mound of earth.

Autumn Song

Narrow women
appear in the forest.
They are tall and lanky,
elongated
bones covered
by skin,
their shoulders
and elbows
knobby,
their fingers
clawed sticks
dangling
from their arms.
They wear
strips of cloth
like bark, their breasts
exposed, their nipples
like knots, their hair
in tatters.

They chant a wavering
song that rises
and falls, reaches in
and pulls out
with the rhythm of their hands
as they rake the past
from under the trees,
in, out, in, out.

The trees sigh.
Their pasts
are gathered, too,
along with
all the forest's remains:
snakeskins, eggshells,
spent cones and dried moss,
bits of fur and feather and bone.

At the end of their song,
the women still themselves.
Brittle and dry,
cracked, crumbling,
they join
the withered and dead,
gathered and given
to the work
of the wind.

Wonder

Garnet stirred in the raw morning chill,
burrowed deeper beneath her blankets.
The room was cold enough to make
thoughts stand still, let wonder set in:

How soil remembered the time for seed,
how water beckoned roots to drink.
How wool knew to sprout from sheep,
and lambs followed the path to birth.

Garnet climbed into Agnes's big bed,
curling into her mother's warmth. Agnes
roused from sleep, nestled the little body,
savored the sweetness of hair and skin.

Sheep be plant of hoof, Garnet declared.
Her certainty bore an echo beyond her
few years. *Yea,* answered Agnes, *ye speak
truth. First lamb of spring we name Plant.*

How Garnet Grew

Agnes saw that Garnet grew
through longings. Met or not,
Garnet's longings reached
toward what she was meant
to understand: a shiny turtle
on a rock by the river, a fallen
baby bird with unfinished
feathers, worlds beyond
clouds and beneath rich soil.
Garnet soaked up all she
encountered like grateful earth
received each passing rain.

Despite her name, Garnet
was a soft and gentle child
whose greatest joy was to be
with small and quiet things,
with the often overlooked.
Sarah called her She Who
Notices. And like her name,
Garnet shone with a fire
that burned bravely, steadily,
a fire that rose from her heart,
warming everything she touched,
her namesake stone made flesh.

Windfall, Early Spring

The forest cleaved open, split
like hardpan, ripped like skin.
Moon and stars blew away.
There was no light.
Bear hid in her cave, fox
in her den. Owl took refuge
in a hollow, swaying trunk.
Last fall's oak leaves still clung
to the branches, rattled like snakes.
All night the house groaned,
as if it recalled the heaving ship.

It was not a time for prayer, unless
prayer is sung by blinded eyes
and taut limbs. It was a time
to know the wind, to feel its force
and enter there, buffered and harbored
by gale and grace, in this body
that has known many years, lived
many storms. To be carried away
by the wind, to fly in its arms
would be an honorable death.

But this is not the time for death.
Wind clears the air, makes way
for new breath. Wind sings
its bold song that demands to be heard.
There is no choice but to listen, to bend.
A dream of wind is just as strong,
cleans the mind and heart. All is
understood, remembered, forgiven.

In this morning's sun, Wind's footprints
and claw marks are everywhere. Cracks
in the windows. Shingles and branches
strewn over the pasture, doors torn
from their hinges. But the air is sweet.
And the silent forest beckons, wanting
to show us the Great Oak still stands,
wanting to show us Wind's offering:
trees who gave themselves to its voice,
who let themselves snap in its hands.
We will have wood for next winter.

Downriver Prayers

Agnes never lost her longing to know
what happened to Johann and Agate.
Two rivers divided them, the one called
Schoharie that was hers and the great one
called Mohawk that had lured them away.

Between them lay waterfalls, some gentle
and quiet, others noisy and boisterous,
the largest plunging from such a height,
it silenced thunder belonging to sky.
Sarah's grandmother spoke of these places
so many times, Agnes could hear them.

Its power threatening to topple her,
Agnes stood firm in her river, sending
prayers from her body through the current,
all the way to Agate and Johann.

The water swept past her and away,
eternally toward them, for her river fed
theirs, far to the north. She knew their toil,
saw each mopping the sweat from his brow
with his shirtsleeve, their smiles echoing
one to the other and back again. And their
serious contemplation of plow and cloud.

Agnes sent her prayers downstream,
wondered if they ever talked of her, if they
remembered, or if they'd closed the door
just as they'd secure the barn against storm.

As currents carried blessings down
the years, Agnes would never know
what befell them, never know they were
taken early by blizzard, their bodies frozen
as hard as the rock that named Agate,
their faces turned in her direction.

Girl Made of Stars

Something tugged the bedding at her back as if to say, *Wake up, come,* so Agnes rose in the unsettled dark.

She slipped from the cabin, sat down on the rock just outside the door. It was the heart of summer, the air moist, beginning to cool from the day's heat. She puzzled over the reason she'd been bidden from sleep, over what to sense and where.

The noises of night were hearty and rich. The longer she sat, the more they voiced, a multitude: batwings fluttering over her head, the quick cry of an owl's sudden meal, the calls of cricket and frog and fox. The river below was shallow and quiet, keeping to itself, but its scent carried up to her.

Fireflies danced around Agnes, sparking and flickering, mirroring the stars above. The new moon was hidden beyond the ridge, its faint glow not yet dusting the valley.

Then she noticed her, the figure of a girl at the edge of the sky. Agnes sat with the noticing until she could see her clearly. She watched as the girl, small and lithe, scampered across cut grass, stopped to gaze at the stars. Agnes listened to the words rising in the girl, in a far place and time yet to be: *I'm alive!*

A star streaked through the sky.

Beyond Time

Where Prayer Creek spoke its loudest,
atop its highest waterfall, Agnes waded
into the water, walked the stone rim

that formed its lip. She had come to offer
a prayer of thanksgiving, for all she had
received, for the generations before her,

for those still to come. The water's force
rumbled the rock beneath her bare feet,
each of her slow steps deliberate, careful.

She sang as she had never sung before,
not in words, but in the sounds and rhythms
of the Old Ways, the Ways of the Mother.

Her whole body was prayer, her mind
was prayer, her voice, her heart. Nearly
halfway across, the rock shelf broke

beneath her, and she tumbled over the edge.
The forest resounded with falling rock,
with the rush of the water's new path.

She was lost in it, a pale speck claimed by
the creek she loved most of all. Welcomed
by the white rattlesnake, Agnes became water.

Part 4
Hour of Seed

Garnet

1765-1775

Visitors

When you dream of the long dead,
they speak of the turnings of moon
and stars, of the way rock holds
all that ever was. Of the depths
of the valleys and where the sun is
before it rises. The long dead do not
sing. Their words are large and slow,
without effort. Their eyes are piercing
and mild. They can see your life before
you live it. If you reach toward them,
they will disappear. If they reach
toward you, let them touch you. They
want to cradle you in their arms.

When you dream of the newly dead,
their eyes are bright, their voices pure.
They stay, not because they fear going.
They stay to meet you in ways they never
could in their hungry flesh. They look
the same, yet something is beginning
to stir their hearts, to take them where
their lives could not. They bear the scars
of having lived, smoothed and healed.
Their bones hold strength enough
to let them speak one more time before
they go, one last thing they want to tell.

When you dream of the living, there are
things they wish you to know, things
that are veiled, things they wish you
to hold for them that they cannot. Your
bodies that are not flesh meet in light
and shadow. Thoughts are spoken without
your tongues. You see each other's hearts
beyond the crust of need, beyond the shell
of fear. You glimpse truths small and large,
understand that nothing is what it seems.

When you dream of the ones you do not
know, pay attention. They have chosen you
among all the dreamers. Open your ears
to what they have to say, follow the paths
they show you, around surprising bends,
up and down perplexing slopes. Do not
question their reasons or attempt to hold
them. They are passing through long enough
to leave you on an unseen path. If you wish
it could be otherwise, they will not come.

When you dream of the lost ones, they will
be restored to you. They will not tell you
where they have been. Look into their eyes
so they can know you see them. If they
allow it, clasp their hands. Whether they
are frail or dense, skittish or solid, let them
go. Just as they could not be held in life,
they cannot be kept in dreams. They come
to teach you what it means to be given.
If you learn, they might come by again.

Clear Water

When you drink of the river, you come to know
its thoughts. You become a changeling, like seeds

transmuted by rain that offer green shoots to the sun.
Clear water allows you to see and hear and speak.

There is nothing between you and truth. The river
knows, and you come to know what the river knows.

Those who came before us understood that Snake
guards the waters. When you drink of the river,

its sinuous movement becomes yours. You glide
like Snake winding over the earth, supple

and strong, eyes all-seeing, all-knowing. Reborn
out of your skin, you remember who you are.

What the Beech Knows

The beech tells a different story,
of wind touching its skin and leaving
no trace. Of sun that ruffles waiting
branches, and leaves that rattle

in changing air. Fox and grouse,
bear and deer tell of its fruits,
the narrow crack that widens,
releases a charm into an open mouth.

If you walk underneath a beech, you will
feel the muscle that holds the land ready.
You will sense how earth breathes the scent
of rain, receives rain's nudge and resolve.

You cannot know all the beech has to say
until you sit upon the rock resting
beneath. For endless turns of the moon
stone has harbored silence, and listened.

Kinds of Light

Before time, when everything was real, there was nothing. Now, in the darkness time, we are meant to see something. There is light in all things, in the acorn Oma carried in her pocket. My mother brought it here, planted it, harvested acorns for years. Some she buried with her babies who never lived, who live now in these oaks, growing taller, leaning in and joining trunks to stand steadier in wind that tears through the valley. Wind speaks and carries the speech of all trees. Listen, you can hear them.

Everything speaks in its own way, speech that is not-words, yet carries all that is spoken. When you breathe, you take it in. When you exhale, you add your own voice. It does not matter if you whisper or roar or if you are silent. Your voice is still part of the language carried by wind to all the far places. If you know this, then you know that you are part of everything, from the tiny ant to the great bear. You know your place, feel it in your blood and bones, your place in the wide expanse that grows only wider.

What you do matters, what you say matters, what you do not do and do not say matters. Everything hears you and feels the spark of you, in the fine hairs of the nettle leaf and the smooth manes of ripe corn. Water caresses, fog sees, and the uppermost reaches of the forest listen. Light and shadow touch your face, are touched by your hands. You move through them, stirring the air they enliven, so you can know the light, the kind that breaks your heart, so sweetly golden.

Inside your heart is more light, the kind that shatters ice and flutters the night sky, or arches across the valley in the day. Or the beat of summer that stuns the air. The kind that glints after rain and tells the leaves when to unfurl or fall. Moonlight in owl's eye. Lightfall beyond shadow in the forest. Murmurs beyond clouds that foretell blue. Inside your heart is love for all things, almost beyond bearing, but you do bear it. Those unknown and unseen by us now will be born into all the light you can hold for them, all the light that will break their hearts, so sweetly golden, and show them what is inside.

Garnet's Prayer

After the fire, pray for healing.
After the flood, pray for healing.
After the bear is found shot near the river,
after the Big Men take all the land,
                              pray for healing.

After the babies die, pray for healing.
After the moon waxes full, pray for healing.
After the sun rises new in the morning,
after a stranger fells the Great Oak,
                              pray for healing.

After the blizzard, pray for healing.
After mice raid the flour bin, pray for healing.
After the sky widens and shines,
after seeds wait in the dark,
                              pray for healing.

After hail batters the roof, pray for healing.
After the geese arrive again, pray for healing.
After a cup of fresh water,
after the moon silvers and sinks,
                              pray for healing.

After weeks without rain, pray for healing.
After the stillborn calf, pray for healing.
After lightning ignites the barn,
after thunder roars through the valley,
                              pray for healing.

After eyes light with laughter, pray for healing.
After an hour's rest, pray for healing.
After the corn grows sweet,
after the hay is cut and brought in,
                    pray for healing.

After dawn crests the ridge, pray for healing.
After our men disappear, pray for healing.
After winter's larder grows scant,
after snow and ice take the sheep,
                    pray for healing.

After sun warms the earth, pray for healing.
After wind tells its stories, pray for healing.
After rocks sing their echoes,
after new shoots reach from the soil,
                    pray for healing.

After a sleepless night, pray for healing.
After the ax is sharpened, pray for healing.
After the firewood is split and stacked,
after the meat has cured,
                    pray for healing.

After a star falls, pray for healing.
After the cow gives no milk, pray for healing.
After the river shrinks from its banks,
after the waterfall thins to a trickle,
                    pray for healing.

After the deerskin is soft, pray for healing.
After wool spins into yarn, pray for healing.
After thick cream turns to butter,
after the chaff flies from the wheat,
                    pray for healing.

After sleep, pray for healing.
After the women speak, pray for healing.
After rain quenches the earth,
after fish make circles in the pool,
                    pray for healing.

After the songs, pray for healing.
After the blanket is woven, pray for healing.
After the medicine is gathered,
after the company of friends,
                    pray for healing.

After the snake sheds its skin, pray for healing.
After the berries ripen, pray for healing.
After any death, after any birth,
after each season gives way to the next,
                    pray for healing.

Miracles

What do you do when you are called?
How do you find your way
when you don't understand where to go?
How do you trust the dawn's strange words,
the nudge in the night,
the owl cry outside the window?

As I crest the steep hill that offers my first glimpse of the Schoharie Creek Valley, I have to pull over. I've never been in this part of upstate New York, yet I know this valley so deeply that it must be recorded in my bones. How I have arrived here is a long story, a whisper in a far longer story that takes me on a nine-year odyssey filled with discovery, mystery, and profound contemplation about time, place, and generational healing.

What do you know about your paternal grandmother? My friend's question leads me to dig out a paper genealogy I received in the mail a decade ago. It's been in a file cabinet for years because I couldn't understand its organization. Sitting in the shade of a bigleaf maple on this hot summer day, I open the booklet. The organization is immediately clear.

I find my father's mother. I trace the generations of her family until I find her earliest female ancestor, *Agnes*

Dietrich. Details are sparse, but I see birthdates in the late 1600s for Agnes's husband and father-in-law and their birthplace near a town called Neuwied. Notes explain that Neuwied was in the Lower Palatinate, a feudal principality in what is now Germany. I see, too, that Agnes's son was born and married in upstate New York. The only information about Agnes herself is a cryptic note about her birthplace: *prob Germany*.

I retrieve a world atlas from the house and scour the map of Germany. When I find Neuwied, the hair on the back of my neck rises and chills run along my spine. My father was a prisoner of war, captured during the Battle of the Bulge in December 1944, and he was force marched eastward in bitter winter conditions from Belgium through Germany to Stalag IV-B, where he was held until his liberation the following May.

My father wasn't much interested in his family history. He knew his ancestors had come to America many generations earlier. He thought they were Dutch. As I trace the route of that grueling forced march, I realize that unknown to him, he passed through the land of his origins.

I'm hungry for information to create Agnes's lived experience. I gather books and internet sources about feudal societies, agriculture in the Rhine River Valley, the role of religion in her time, the practice of traditional folk beliefs, the realities of feudal women's lives.

Miracles

What came before that? I ask this question over and over, leading me earlier and earlier, all the way back to neolithic and paleolithic cultures. Everything I read and see, even seemingly unrelated fiction that attracts me, feeds my hunger to imagine Agnes's life.

I discover the pioneering work of archeologist Marija Gimbutas, focusing on the neolithic cultures of Europe. At the same time, I happen to read an interview with Leslie Marmon Silko, in which she discusses her interest in Europe's indigenous people. I'm also reading one of Silko's novels. In a note on the last page about the sources of the many-layered story, she mentions that her German translator gave her a book about the neolithic goddess cultures of Old Europe. From scenes in the novel, I know she's referring to Gimbutas's work.

Historical information and another novel I'm reading create a similar intersection, and the Gundestrup Cauldron enters Agnes's story. When I learn that a piece of the great cauldron remains missing, I begin to ask, *What if. What if the missing piece could tell a story?*

One source leads me to another. At just the right moment, I stumble on a book called, *Becoming German*, which tells the story of Agnes and her people, of the mass emigration of Palatines from the Rhine Valley, of the arduous three-year journey that takes them, finally, to Schoharie Creek.

Everything I encounter is woven together, telling me I'm on the right path, a path with dozens of twists and turns. I don't understand where I'm going, but I'm learning to trust where I'm led.

I'm immersed in my research when my husband Barry and I decide to sell our too-large house in the country and find a smaller one in town. I pack the books I've collected and the notebooks I've filled and label the large box *Agnes*. I've started to write about her but keep hitting dead ends. Something important eludes me, so I've stopped.

I wake one morning in the new house. Barry is out of town. As I open my eyes to the dim and quiet room, I hear a voice, a woman's voice, speaking slowly in broken English: *Every day I dig rocks. If rocks be potatoes, I eat them.*

My heart pounds as I grab my notebook and pen. She goes on to tell a brief story, and I write down her words as she speaks. I have no doubt about who she is.

It's mid-October. To jumpstart my work on the Agnes project after our move, I rent a condo on the Oregon coast for a writing retreat. I load the car with meals Barry has made for me, my Agnes books and notebooks, rain gear, laptop, fresh pens, blank notebooks, candles, bubble bath, warm clothes, good coffee, a novel, a bottle of wine, chocolate, my hopes.

Settled in, I open the window a crack so I can hear the ocean. I'm a couple of blocks from the water but I have a second-story view. The weather is so wild a staff member brings me a battery lantern, but the power never goes out. Each day there's a break in the rain that allows me to roam the beach. One night I walk under a full moon. I create ceremonies to open myself to what might come. I take a bubble bath, savor a glass of wine. I read. I look through my notes. I write about writing. I write about my fears. I write about rain and wind.

On the day before I'm to check out and go home, I sit with my morning coffee, my notebook and pen. I write a sentence, then another. It turns into a page. I take a deep breath, sip my coffee. I know I have her now. I have Agnes.

There comes a time when research isn't enough, so I book a trip to upstate New York. I need to see the area where Agnes lived, to walk where she might have walked, breathe the air, smell the scents, listen to the sounds, feel the land under my feet. I need to visit Schoharie Creek.

I fly to Connecticut, where I celebrate a friend's retirement. From there, I head toward New York. On the way, I park my rental car at the entrance to the small cemetery in western Connecticut where my father's parents are buried. I've never been here, so I've called ahead to ask the caretaker where to find their graves, startled when a man's voice answers with the name of a paint store, but he assures me I have the right person. I hear him leafing through record books until he finds their names.

My grandfather died the year before I was born. My grandmother died at age thirty-five. My father was five when he lost her. Her marker is tiny, made of concrete, her name wearing away.

In New York, just over the state line from Connecticut, I pull into the cemetery where my grandmother's parents are buried. There's no online contact information, just a photo of the gate, so I know only its name. It's huge, and I drive its looping dirt roads bewildered. There is no one here to ask. I head back to the entrance, find a shady spot to park, vow to be patient. I'll start in the middle of the first loop, look at every headstone in concentric circles, and then move on to the next. I walk up the grassy rise to the first loop's center, survey the cemetery that extends as far as I can see. Then I look down. My great-grandparents' graves are at my feet.

My last stop for the day is a cemetery described in detail in the genealogy booklet. There's even a hand-drawn map. Several generations of my grandmother's family lie here, going back to my 4th-great-grandparents. I visit each headstone noted on the little map, thirteen in all. Some are barely readable, their letters worn away. Others are cracked. Three are broken, repaired with cement reinforced by rusted metal strips. A few remain in pieces, propped against each other. The oldest is only two generations away from Agnes.

In each of these cemeteries, a large tree grows near my ancestors' graves. All three trees have shed some of their bark, the pieces scattered around their ancient trunks. At each site I cup a piece of bark in my palm. Their bodies fed these trees. My gratitude travels down the generations, down the lineage that allows me to live.

The first full day of my stay in New York I'm invited for morning coffee with my host. She's listening to my explanation of why I'm here and my plans so far. I'm telling her about the appointments I've made at the New York State Museum in Albany and my plan to visit the Iroquois Museum located in the town of Howes Cave. Just then her husband walks through the kitchen as he's getting ready for a day of teaching history at a nearby community college. He stops and tells me that I should search online because there's a Mohawk community not far away. He gathers his things and heads off for work.

I can't write about Agnes and the Palatine immigrants without acknowledging the importance of the Haudenosaunee (Iroquois) people they encountered, particularly the Mohawk, the easternmost nation of the Haudenosaunee Confederacy. The immigrants bought their land in the Schoharie Valley from Mohawk people. Yet I also know I can't appropriate information or a point of view that is not mine.

My host's husband's passing comment opens a door to Kanatsiohareke Mohawk Community, a place I doubt I would have found on my own. In 1993 founder and spiritual leader Tom Porter led the effort to re-establish a Mohawk community on traditional lands on the banks of the Mohawk River. Visiting Kanatsiohareke gives me the chance to meet Tom Porter, well known and respected throughout Indian Country and an elder with such generosity of spirit that I can't believe my good fortune.

In our conversation, I ask him about the truth of what has come down through descendants of Palatine immigrants—

that these settlers and Mohawk people lived in peace. I tell him I don't know if this is whitewashed history or fact. In answer, he teaches me about the Great Law, explaining that the story is true. The cultural values of the Great Law made it so. He tells me about the Haudenosaunee Confederacy, showing me a replica of the wampum belt that records its history. And he weaves this telling with the Haudenosaunee creation story because they are the same story.

The Iroquois Museum, built in the shape of a longhouse, is not a big building, at least as far as museums go. When I pay my modest entrance fee, I have no idea of the experience that awaits me inside. Most people visit for an hour or two, but I end up spending all day. Historical and cultural artifacts are displayed alongside the fine work of contemporary Haudenosaunee artists. Every inch holds treasures.

Staffing the entrance desk is Onondaga Nation elder Brenda LaForme. I ask her the same question I asked Tom Porter. She, too, teaches me about the Great Law. She, too, tells me that the story about peaceful coexistence is true.

The peace created by the Great Law and by Palatine resistance to British colonial power would have framed Agnes's life. But it lasted only a few generations. Eventually, governmental pressures and conflicting values in subsequent Palatine generations destroyed it. The span of Agnes's lifetime was also a period of great transition, loss, and dislocation for Mohawk people.

As my day unfolds within the museum, I keep bumping into Brenda, and we continue our conversation. We listen to each other. There is pain in our stories, and healing. There is space enough to hold both.

I end my visit in the gallery that features displays about Mohawk steelworkers, about the generations who worked on the Chrysler Building, the Empire State Building, the World Trade Center, and many others. And about the generation that worked following 9/11 to dismantle the wreckage of the twin towers their grandfathers had built.

Using old-fashioned paper road maps, I locate a few sections of Schoharie Creek accessible by car. The best view is on a high concrete bridge that crosses the river downstream from a wide bend. It's summer and the water is low, but I've read about devastating floods, about the yards-thick rich soil those floods have left behind. From the middle of the bridge, I look upstream at the piled trees torn out by their roots and deposited at the river's curve.

Driving through the rolling hills of farmland within Schoharie Valley, I find my way to one of its tributaries. This creek is named for some local personage, and there's a nature preserve where I can walk a trail alongside it. The air smells like wet earth and pine. A breeze carries over the water and rustles the trees around me. The creek descends gradually, then precipitously to the Schoharie. Riffles and waterfalls sound their cadences. I'm alone here, step lightly, feel presences I can't name. Eventually, when I write about this place, it becomes Agnes's Prayer Creek. At the creek's highest waterfall, vertigo rushes in, takes all my senses away. I see Agnes's death.

To save my phone's battery, I use a digital camera to take photos along the trail, download them to my laptop that evening. Later during the trip, I try to go to that preserve again, but the road isn't there anymore. Months later when my new laptop is synced with my phone, I discover those photos have vanished.

One Friday evening I notice a narrow lane that leaves the main road at an angle. There's a sign for the Old Stone Fort Museum. It's been a long day, but I can't resist. I encounter an imposing stone building on my left, its front yard filled with cannons and monuments. Across the street are several old buildings, moved from locations within Schoharie Valley. A house and a barn catch my eye. I peek in the windows, wander the grounds.

That night I discover online that the buildings are open to the public. And the house, closed for restoration, can be seen by appointment. I call first thing Monday morning and set up a time with Curator Daniel Beams. I figure the busy man will give me a brief look at the house, and then on my own I'll tour the rest of the buildings. But that's not what happens.

Dan Beams spends hours with me. He begins with ice age Schoharie Valley. Over millennia, glaciers clipped the tops of rock mountains. Gouged the land. Created a huge primordial lake. In the last ice age, a glacier retreated north,

Miracles

melting a great dam of ice, releasing a ferocious flood. In its wake, a broad fertile valley.

With Dan's stories, the two-room Palatine house transforms. Cracked mud and lath walls take on their original thin layers of plaster, painted white. Wooden uprights framing each section of wall regain their red paint. Fire heats the central stone fireplace and oven, coals glowing hot and red.

Before long, Agnes moves through the house. She hangs herbs to dry in the loft. Proofs dough on the wide, elevated hearth. Tests the oven's readiness with a quick reach inside its iron door. On the crane, she hangs kettles and pots to bubble and simmer within the deep fireplace. Sunlight pours from the two windows, made brighter by white walls.

Next, Dan brings the barn to life. Its front has a door for horses, another for cows. The double door in the middle is for the wagon. The small one is for people. Inside, the plow awaits spring. Mathooks and siths, forerunners of scythes, are poised to harvest wheat, flails to thresh it against the floor. Tossed in the riddle, wheat kernels settle and chaff flies out the open back doors. Holes high in the eaves, at first glance decoration, let birds come inside. Martins feast on pesky insects. Owls hunt rodents.

A mainstay during my time in New York is a woman named Bonita Humphrey. She runs a small restaurant located down a steep hill and around the corner from where I'm staying. I get coffee there every morning. My research days are long, but when I have time I get breakfast there, too. Bonita chats with me each morning, and I tell her what I discovered in my travels the day before. She works a 96-hour week, yet she's never rushed, always interested, and some mornings she opens the door early so I can get my coffee and be on my way. The last thing I do before I leave town to head back to Connecticut is to ask if I can take her picture. I still have that photo. As always, Bonita is smiling.

Before my New York trip, I contact Dorothy, my nephew's mother-in-law. We've never met because we've never been in the same locale at the same time. Everyone in my family has always said we would like each other. She lives not far from where I'll be staying, and we arrange to spend a day together. The family predictions turn out to be true—it's as if I've found my long-lost sister.

While I'm in upstate New York, I have dream after vivid dream, some beautiful and gentle, others fearsome and powerful. In one dream I meet an old Native woman who welcomes me, feeds me, gives me a stone for protection, transforms my fear.

Although Dorothy knows nothing about this dream, months later she sends me a rock, a garnet from that region of New York. It's exactly the stone from my dream.

The land I wander in upstate New York, filled with presences and ancient memories, does its work on me.

When friends ask me about the trip, the only thing I can find to say is, *Something happened to me there.*

Five years later, Barry and I travel to Denmark to visit friends. The trip makes possible a pilgrimage I never dreamed I'd get to make, to see the Gundestrup Cauldron in the National Museum in Copenhagen.

No one can be certain why the silver plates that make up the Pre-Roman Iron Age cauldron were taken apart and ritually buried in a bog in Jutland, the part of Denmark that shares a border with Germany. Experts have established that its construction is missing one piece.

The cauldron is alone in the room, inside its tall glass case, with low lighting that enhances its shadows and curves. At times, other visitors wander through and stop to look, but mostly I am the only person here. I walk around and around it, peer inside, breathe.

My photos, obscured by shadows and reflections, can't capture what I come to know in its presence. There's one photo I keep, of an ethereal me rising from the cauldron's interior.

That night in my journal I write, *The Cauldron holds the soul of the world.*

Two days after I spend time with the cauldron, I'm resting in the shade of an oak in our Danish friends' back yard, breathing deeply, relaxed. I close my eyes and a purple glow begins to form, growing stronger and stronger. Inside the glow, a woman's eyes gradually appear, then her nose and mouth and chin. Her face is full, her features fine. Our eyes meet. Agnes fades, comes back several times, her left eye always coming first into focus. A shaft of sunlight through the oak leaves brightens her face one last time before she disappears.

Two nights later, I dream of an old woman. We are seated side by side, cross-legged and still, our backs straight. Her hair is white and silky, her skin weathered. Oma and I sit together for a long time in silence.

There's an ancient burial mound, completely covered by earth, in the middle of our friends' property in Denmark, one of the 43,000 estimated to be scattered throughout the countryside. I take daily walks there, stand on its crest looking out at the stony beach, at the sea, at the meadow around me. Wind bends the grasses, raises scents of hay and wildflowers and kelp.

Near the end of our visit, a thunderstorm jolts me awake in the night. Open farmland outside my window lets me see the whole of each jagged bolt, from cloud to ground. Barn and trees flash, then vanish. Thunder vibrates the floor under my feet. In the morning I learn that the lightning set fire to a stack of hay bales in a neighboring field.

The next day, our last one in Denmark, our friend takes us to see a Bronze Age burial mound. This one is exposed.

Miracles

There is a stone circle defining the wide space. In the center is a tight circle of boulders, their sides touching, with a larger flat boulder balanced on top, sheltering what is buried beneath. There are voices here.

It comes unannounced. As I print these final pages and, for the first time, hold in my hands the completed manuscript that will become this book, lightning splits the sky. Everything outside my window pulses with vibrant light. Thunder roars in wave upon wave, reverberating against the walls of the house, rattling the windows. Then, as suddenly as it came, the storm is gone.

A few weeks later as I finish the final proofing of the manuscript and send it off to the designer, sun edges the clouds that have been gathering all afternoon. For hours in the evening, distant lightning flashes and thunder rumbles. In the night the storm arrives here. A rushing downpour and crashing thunder startle me awake. I head outside. Again and again, lightning cracks the sky open. Thunder booms its answer. Dry earth and parched trees welcome the rain.

Thank you, Agnes.

Research

Names and titles listed were current at the time of my consultations in 2017.

Herkimer County Historical Society
Herkimer, New York
Staff and Volunteers
Access to the library and to the historical collections on display

Iroquois Indian Museum
Howes Cave, New York
Brenda LaForme, Onondaga Nation Elder, Volunteer
Discussions of The Great Law and legacies within families and peoples across generations

Kanatsiohareke Mohawk Community
Fonda, New York
Tom Porter (Sakokweniónkwas), Bear Clan Elder of the Mohawk Nation, Community Founder, Spokesperson and Spiritual Leader
Discussions of The Great Law and the creation of the Haudenosaunee (Iroquois) Confederacy

Little Falls Historical Society
Little Falls, New York
Louie Baum, Director
Jeffrey Gressler, President and Director
Pat Gressler, Volunteer
Discussions of Palatine history in the Schoharie and Mohawk Valleys, history of the Mohawk River and the Erie Canal, and access to historical documents and collections

National Museum of Denmark
Copenhagen, Denmark
Exhibit of and information about the Gundestrup Cauldron and access to displayed collections of prehistoric and Pre-Roman Iron Age artifacts

New York State Museum
Albany, New York
Dr. Gwendolyn Saul, Curator of Ethnography
Molly Scofield, Ethnology Research and Collections Technician
Dr. Jennifer Lemak, Chief Curator of History
Robyn Gibson, History Research and Collections Technician
Ralph Rataul, Archaeology Collections Technician
History, ethnography and archaeology discussions and access to collections not on display in the museum

Old Stone Fort Museum
Schoharie, New York
Daniel Beams, Curator
Discussions of the history of Schoharie Valley, including its ice age formation, domestic and farming practices of Palatines, and details of early Palatine immigrant life

184

References

I consulted many books and resources, but those listed here were most important as my research evolved.

Alexander, Gordon A., compilator. *The Family of Hiram Fritz: A Genealogy of Hiram Fritz, 1814.* Private publication for descendants, 1993.

Barber, Elizabeth Wayland. *Women's Work, the First 20,000 Years: Women, Cloth, and Society in Early Times.* New York: W. W. Norton & Company, 1994.

Bonaparte, Darren. *Creation & Confederation: The Living History of the Iroquois.* Ahkwesáhsne Mohawk Territory: The Wampum Chronicles, 2006.

The Decolonial Atlas. decolonialatlas.wordpress.com

Ferguson, John P. *The Schoharie Mohawks.* Howes Cave, New York: Iroquois Indian Museum, 2009.

Gimbutas, Marija. *The Goddesses and Gods of Old Europe, 6500-3500 BC: Myths and Cult Images.* Berkeley and Los Angeles: University of California Press, 1982.

---. *The Language of the Goddess.* New York: Thames & Hudson Inc., 1989. Reprinted 2006.

The Brothers Grimm. *Grimm's Complete Fairy Tales.*
Trans. Margaret Hunt. San Diego: Canterbury
Classics, 2011.

Herrick, James W. *Iroquois Medical Botany.* Ed. and
Foreword by Dean R. Snow. Syracuse: Syracuse
University Press, 1995.

Jakobsdóttir, Svava. *Gunnlöth's Tale.* Trans. Oliver Watts.
London: Norvik Press, 2011.

Mann, Barbara Alice. *Iroquoian Women: The Gantowisas.*
Foreword by Paula Gunn Allen. New York: Peter
Lang, 2000.

Otterness, Philip. *Becoming German: The 1709 Palatine
Migration to New York.* Ithaca: Cornell University
Press, 2004.

Porter, Thomas R. (Sakokweniónkwas), Bear Clan Elder of
the Mohawk Nation. *And Grandma Said... Iroquois
Teachings as passed down through the oral
tradition.* Ed. Lesley Forrester. Xlibris Corporation,
2008.

Schiff, Stacy. *The Witches: Salem, 1692.* New York: Little,
Brown and Company, 2015.

Silko, Leslie Marmon. "An Interview with Leslie Marmon
Silko." Interview conducted by Thomas Irmer,
Alt-X Berlin/Leipzig correspondent. altx.com,
1995.

---. *Gardens in the Dunes*. New York: Simon & Schuster Paperbacks, 1999.

Wagner, Sally Roesch. *Sisters in Spirit: Haudenosaunee (Iroquois) Influence on Early American Feminists*. Summertown, Tennessee: Native Voices, 2001.

Gratitude

"Auguries of Things to Come" appeared in the Summer/ Fall 2022 issue of *Naugatuck River Review*.

"Night Keepers" is forthcoming in summer 2023 in the Crone Lit anthology, *Wild Crone Wisdom: Poetry and Stories*, published by Wild Librarian Press.

"Visitors" is forthcoming in the Fall/Winter 2024 edition of *Soul-Lit: a journal of spiritual poetry*.

For hosting me in Connecticut, for many laughs, and for mystical journeys: Deb Shea.

For hosting me in Denmark, for guided tours, for family celebrations, and for amazing food: Heidi Bojsen and Esben Christensen.

For hosting me in New York, for providing guidance and resources, and for treating me to ice cream and homemade muffins: Teri and Al Chace.

For being my mainstay in New York: Bonita Humphrey, owner of Bonita's Sandwich Chef, Little Falls, NY.

For unfailing support of me and my work: Sydne Cogburn, Christine Cole, Deb Geer, Lee Graves (*in memoriam*),

Karen Harding, Arlene Johnson, Dean and Carla Jones, Dodie Jordan, Brenda Kaulback, Robin Lester, Carol Millette, Marjorie Power, JJ Nettlekiss, Kay Ridgway, Dorothy Sardella, Carol Steele, Joan Swanson, Jane Tarnauskas, Sandy Yannone.

For glorious cover and book design: Debi Bodett.

For being my Poetry Sister, for her feedback on many of these poems, and for lifting my spirit always: Joanne Clarkson.

For writing the world back to its soul, for her uncanny editing, and for living this book with me: June O'Brien.

And for teaching me all I know about love: Barry Troutman.

About the Author

Linda Strever is the author of *My Life in Cars* (poetry), *Against My Dreams* (poetry) and *Don't Look Away* (fiction). Her poetry has been published in numerous journals and anthologies. Winner of the Lois Cranston Memorial Poetry Prize and a Pushcart Prize nominee, her work has been a finalist for the New Issues Poetry Prize, the Levis Poetry Prize, the Ohio State University Press Award in Poetry, and the Eludia Award in fiction. She has an MFA from Brooklyn College, has worked as a proofreader, editor, graphic artist, teacher, trainer and mediator, and lives in the Pacific Northwest.

Made in the USA
Middletown, DE
26 September 2023

39237925R00123